BENCHMARK SERIES

Microsoft® Access®

2016
Level 2

Workbook

Davidson

St. Paul

Senior Vice President	Linda Hein
Editor in Chief	Christine Hurney
Director of Production	Timothy W. Larson
Production Editor	Jen Weaverling
Cover and Text Designer	Valerie King
Copy Editors	Communicáto, Ltd.
Senior Design and Production Specialist	Jack Ross
Design and Production Specialist	PerfecType
Assistant Developmental Editors	Mamie Clark, Katie Werdick
Testers	Janet Blum, Fanshawe College; Traci Post
Instructional Support Writers	Janet Blum, Fanshawe College; Brienna McWade
Indexer	Terry Casey
Vice President Information Technology	Chuck Bratton
Digital Projects Manager	Tom Modl
Vice President Sales and Marketing	Scott Burns
Director of Marketing	Lara Weber McLellan

Trademarks: Microsoft is a trademark or registered trademark of Microsoft Corporation in the United States and/or other countries. Some of the product names and company names included in this book have been used for identification purposes only and may be trademarks or registered trade names of their respective manufacturers and sellers. The authors, editors, and publisher disclaim any affiliation, association, or connection with, or sponsorship or endorsement by, such owners.

We have made every effort to trace the ownership of all copyrighted material and to secure permission from copyright holders. In the event of any question arising as to the use of any material, we will be pleased to make the necessary corrections in future printings.

Cover Photo Credits: © Photomall/Dreamstime.com

Paradigm Publishing is independent from Microsoft Corporation, and not affiliated with Microsoft in any manner. While this publication may be used in assisting individuals to prepare for a Microsoft Office Specialist certification exam, Microsoft, its designated program administrator, and Paradigm Publishing do not warrant that use of this publication will ensure passing a Microsoft Office Specialist certification exam.

ISBN 978-0-76386-957-1 (digital)
ISBN 978-0-76387-179-6 (print)

© 2017 by Paradigm Publishing, Inc.
875 Montreal Way
St. Paul, MN 55102
Email: educate@emcp.com
Website: ParadigmCollege.com

All rights reserved. No part of this publication may be adapted, reproduced, stored in a retrieval system, or transmitted in any form or by any means, electronic, mechanical, photocopying, recording, or otherwise, without prior written permission from the publisher.

Printed in the United States of America

24 23 22 21 20 19 18 17 16   2 3 4 5 6 7 8 9 10 11 12

Contents

ACCESS 2016

Unit 1
Advanced Tables, Relationships, Queries and Forms — 1

Chapter 1	Designing the Structure of Tables	3
Chapter 2	Building Relationships and Lookup Fields	9
Chapter 3	Advanced Query Techniques	15
Chapter 4	Creating and Using Custom Forms	21
	Unit 1 Performance Assessment	29

Unit 2
Advanced Reports, Access Tools, and Customizing Access — 37

Chapter 5	Creating and Using Custom Reports	39
Chapter 6	Using Access Tools and Managing Objects	45
Chapter 7	Automating, Customizing, and Securing Access	51
Chapter 8	Integrating Access Data	57
	Unit 2 Performance Assessment	61

Microsoft® Access® Level 2

Unit 1

Advanced Tables, Relationships, Queries, and Forms

Chapter 1 Designing the Structure of Tables

Chapter 2 Building Relationships and Lookup Fields

Chapter 3 Advanced Query Techniques

Chapter 4 Creating and Using Custom Forms

Unit 1 Performance Assessment

Microsoft® Access®
Designing the Structure of Tables

CHAPTER 1

Study Tools

Study tools include a presentation and a list of chapter Quick Steps and Hint margin notes. Use these resources to help you further develop and review skills learned in this chapter.

Concepts Check

Check your understanding by identifying application tools used in this chapter. If you are a SNAP user, launch the Concepts Check from your Assignments page.

Recheck

Check your understanding by taking this quiz. If you are a SNAP user, launch the Recheck from your Assignments page.

Skills Exercise

Additional activities are available to SNAP users. If you are a SNAP user, access these activities from your Assignments page.

Skills Assessment

Assessment 1

Create a New Database

1. Create a new blank database named **1-BenchmarkGolf.accdb**.
2. Create the tables shown in Figure WB-1.1 to store membership records for the Benchmark Golf and Country Club. Be sure to set the primary key field and assign data types and field sizes.
3. Close any tables that have been left open.

Figure WB-1.1 Assessment 1

Members		
*MemberID	Short Text	3
FName	Short Text	20
LName	Short Text	30
Street	Short Text	35
City	Short Text	25
State	Short Text	2
ZIP	Short Text	10
HPhone	Short Text	14
CPhone	Short Text	14
BirthDate	Date/Time	
Category	Short Text	10
FamilyMem	Yes/No	

FamilyMembers		
*FamilyMemID	Short Text	3
MemberID	Short Text	3
FName	Short Text	20
LName	Short Text	30
BirthDate	Date/Time	
SocialMem	Yes/No	

MemberTypes		
*Category	Short Text	10
AnnualFee	Currency	
MonthlyFee	Currency	
Restrictions	Long Text	

3

Assessment 2 — Add Captions and Disallow Blank Values

1. With **1-BenchmarkGolf.accdb** open, create captions for the fields as follows:

   Members Table

Field Name	Caption
MemberID	ID Number
FName	First Name
LName	Last Name
Street	Street Address
ZIP	ZIP Code
HPhone	Home Phone
CPhone	Cell Phone
BirthDate	Birth Date
FamilyMem	Family Member?

   FamilyMembers Table

Field Name	Caption
FamilyMemID	Family ID Number
MemberID	Member ID Number
FName	First Name
LName	Last Name
BirthDate	Birth Date
SocialMem	Social Member?

   MemberTypes Table

Field Name	Caption
AnnualFee	Annual Fee
MonthlyFee	Monthly Fee

2. Make the *ZIP* field a required field and disallow zero-length strings.
3. Save and then close all the tables.

Assessment 3 — Create Custom Formats and Input Masks

1. With **1-BenchmarkGolf.accdb** open, create the following custom formats:
   a. Display the state text in uppercase characters.
   b. Display all birth dates with the month in abbreviated form, followed by the day of the month as two digits and the year as four digits. Use single spaces to separate the sections.
   c. Display the monthly fee in blue with two digits past the decimal point. The decimal values will show zeros if a zero is entered.
2. Create the following custom input masks:
   a. In the *MemberID* fields in the Members table and the FamilyMembers table, require all three digits, display the underscore character as the placeholder, and do not store the display characters.
   b. Require the *ZIP* field in the Members table to be entered in the pattern of five required digits followed by a hyphen and then four required digits. Display the pound symbol (#) as the placeholder and do not store the display characters.
   c. Use the Input Mask Wizard to create the standard input mask for the two telephone fields in the Members table. Do not store the display characters. When the mask is finished, edit the codes in the property to make the three characters in the area code required digits, as opposed to the optional digits that the wizard created.

d. Create an input mask for both *BirthDate* fields that will match the custom format pattern created in Step 1b, except use hyphens between the sections. Store the display characters in the field and display the underscore character as the placeholder. For example, the custom format should display the date as *May 03 1964* in the datasheet. ***Hints: Do not worry about the first letter of the month being uppercase, since the Format property will automatically apply proper capitalization. Also, once the input mask has been created correctly, the entry can be copied and pasted to the other*** **BirthDate** ***field***.

3. Save and then close all the tables.

Assessment 4

Add Records

1. With **1-BenchmarkGolf.accdb** open, add the following records. Type the text in the *State* field as shown to test the format code. As you type the zip codes, telephone numbers, and dates, be careful to watch the placeholders and to enter data in the required pattern.

Members Table

Field	Record 1	Record 2
ID Number	100	110
First Name	Hilary	Jesse
Last Name	Sampson	Reynolds
Street Address	300 S Saguaro Drive	7229 E University Drive
City	Apache Junction	Mesa
State	Az	Az
ZIP Code	85220 4956	85207 6501
Home Phone	602 555 1587	480 555 1385
Cell Phone	602 555 3496	480 555 1699
Birth Date	May 03 1964	Oct 15 1977
Category	Gold	Silver
Family Member?	Yes	No

FamilyMembers Table

Field	Record 1	Record 2
Family ID Number	F61	F62
Member ID Number	100	100
First Name	Kayla	Roy
Last Name	Sampson	Sampson
Birth Date	Jul 18 1999	Mar 16 2001
Social Member?	No	No

MemberTypes Table

Field	Record 1	Record 2	Record 3
Category	Gold	Silver	Bronze
Annual Fee	4500	3775	2550
Monthly Fee	170	120	99
Restrictions	Unlimited weekdays and weekends; weekend ballot first	Unlimited weekdays; weekend ballot second	Unlimited weekdays; weekends after 3 p.m.

2. Adjust all the column widths to best fit and then print each table in landscape orientation. *Note: The Members table will print on two pages*.
3. Close any tables that have been left open, saving layout changes.
4. Close **1-BenchmarkGolf.accdb**.

Visual Benchmark

Create a New Database

1. Create a new blank database named **1-PawsParadise.accdb**.
2. Create the tables shown in the database diagram in Figure WB-1.2, including setting the primary key field and assigning data types and field sizes. The tables are to be used by Paws Paradise Boarding Inc. to store the records of dog owners, dogs, and kennel categories.
3. Analyze the datasheets shown in Figure WB-1.3 and make the necessary changes to field properties. The datasheets show the captions, default values, custom formats, and rich text formatting in the records. Use the following information to set other field properties not visible in the datasheet:
   a. Make *ZIP* a required field and then use the Input Mask Wizard to create the default input mask for a zip code. Store the display characters.
   b. Use the Input Mask Wizard to create the default input masks for both telephone fields and then edit the masks to change the area code to three required digits. Store the display characters.
4. Add the records shown in the datasheets to the tables.
5. Adjust all the column widths to best fit and then print each table in landscape orientation. *Note: The DogOwners and Dogs tables will print on two pages. Change the left and right margins of the KennelCategories table to be 0.5 inch.*
6. Save and then close all the tables.
7. Close the **1-PawsParadise.accdb** database.

Figure WB-1.2 Visual Benchmark Database Diagram

DogOwners

Field	Type	Size
*CustNum	Short Text	3
FName	Short Text	20
LName	Short Text	30
Street	Short Text	35
City	Short Text	25
State	Short Text	2
ZIP	Short Text	10
HPhone	Short Text	14
EPhone	Short Text	14
MultipleDogs	Yes/No	

Dogs

Field	Type	Size
*DogID	AutoNumber	
CustNum	Short Text	3
DogName	Short Text	20
Breed	Short Text	50
Color	Short Text	20
Bordetella	Yes/No	
Rabies	Yes/No	
Play	Yes/No	
KennelCat	Short Text	7

KennelCategories

Field	Type	Size
*KennelCat	Short Text	7
Type	Short Text	25
Descr	Long Text	
DailyRate	Currency	

Figure WB-1.3 Visual Benchmark Datasheets

DogOwners

Customer Number	First Name	Last Name	Street Address	City	State	ZIP Code	Home Telephone	Emergency Telephone	Multiple Dogs?
100	Shawn	Jenkins	101 Davis Street	Bradford	PA	16701-	(814) 555-8446	(814) 555-7469	☑
110	Valerie	McTague	12 Bishop Street	Bradford	PA	16701-	(814) 555-3456	(814) 555-1495	☐
115	Glen	Waters	35 Vista Avenue	Bradford	PA	16701-2760	(814) 555-7496	(814) 555-6124	☐
*				Bradford	PA				☐

Dogs

Dog ID	Customer Number	Dog's Name	Breed	Color	Bordetella Vaccine Checked?	Rabies Vaccine Checked?	Play with other dogs?	Kennel Category
1	100	Abby	Labrador Retriever	Black	☑	☑	☑	VIP
2	100	Winnie	Cocker Spaniel	Buff	☑	☑	☑	VIP
3	110	Chloe	Poodle	White	☑	☑	☐	Deluxe
4	115	Barney	Pug	Black	☐	☐	☐	InOut
* (New)					☑	☑	☑	

KennelCategories

Kennel Category	Kennel Type	Description	Daily Rate
DayCare	Day Care Boarding	Grassy play area where dogs can play with staff and other dogs throughout the day.	$16.50
Deluxe	Deluxe Suite	Designed for *geriatric or special needs dogs*. Raised beds and quiet location.	$29.50
InOut	Indoor/Outdoor Suite	Indoor kennel attached to covered outdoor patio.	$25.50
VIP	V.I.P. Suite	*Indoor upgraded kennel* attached to covered outdoor patio and grass play area.	$38.50

Case Study

Part 1

You work as an intern at Bestar Plumbing Service. Examine the customer invoice shown in Figure WB-1.4. The owners would like to create an Access database that includes all of the information in the invoice. Design tables for the data using the invoice and the following additional information from the owner:

- Each customer number is assigned using the first three letters of the customer's last name (all uppercase) followed by a hyphen character and three digits.
- Some invoices include the cost of plumbing parts plus labor charges. Individual parts are not itemized on the customer invoice. The service technician enters all the parts used on a single line on the invoice.
- Bestar has two hourly labor rates: $61.75 for a senior service technician and $38.00 for an apprentice technician.

Using Microsoft Word, create a document that diagrams the tables, including table names, field names, data types, and field sizes. Use an asterisk to denote the primary key field in each table. Ask your instructor for the required format of the diagram (for instance, using text boxes or tables in Word) or whether a handwritten diagram is acceptable. Save the Word document and name it **1-BestarPlumbing**. Save, print, and then close **1-BestarPlumbing.docx**.

Figure WB-1.4 Case Study, Part 1

BPS
Bestar Plumbing Service

43 Valley Way
Madison, WI 53710
608-555-7575
bestar@emcp.net

INVOICE

INVOICE NO. 1001
DATE 4/24/2018
CUSTOMER ID COL-104

TO Diane Coleman
2101 Lakeland Avenue
Madison, WI 53704
608-555-9995

TERMS Due on receipt

QUANTITY	DESCRIPTION	UNIT PRICE	LINE TOTAL
1 hr	Service call to repair burst water pipe	$61.75	$61.75
	Service Technician: Jose Martinez		
	Date of Service: April 23, 2018		
		SUBTOTAL	$61.75
		(5%) SALES TAX	$3.09
		TOTAL DUE	**$126.59**

Part 2 Using the table diagram created in Part 1, create a new database named **1-BestarPlumbing.accdb** and then create the tables for the database. Set the primary key field and assign data types and field sizes.

Part 3 Consider what field properties can be used to ensure data integrity and consistency. Modify the field properties to restrict data accepted into the field and to display the data after it has been accepted. Use the data in Figure WB-1.4 to enter a sample record in each table to test the field properties. Print each table on one page with all the column widths set to best fit. Change the page orientation to landscape and the margins to 0.25 inch if necessary.

Microsoft® Access®
Building Relationships and Lookup Fields

CHAPTER 2

Study Tools

Study tools include a presentation and a list of chapter Quick Steps and Hint margin notes. Use these resources to help you further develop and review skills learned in this chapter.

Concepts Check

Check your understanding by identifying application tools used in this chapter. If you are a SNAP user, launch the Concepts Check from your Assignments page.

Recheck

Check your understanding by taking this quiz. If you are a SNAP user, launch the Recheck from your Assignments page.

Skills Exercise

Additional activities are available to SNAP users. If you are a SNAP user, access these activities from your Assignments page.

Skills Assessment

Assessment 1

Data Files

Create a Lookup List

1. Open **2-ViewRite.accdb** and enable the content.
2. Open all the tables in Datasheet view and review the fields and records to become familiar with the database. Close all the tables when finished.
3. Open the Relationships window and close the Show Table dialog box if necessary. Notice that no relationships have been created in the database. Close the Relationships window.
4. The *CustID* field in the WebOrders table can be made easier to use by changing it to a lookup list that presents customer names and numbers from the *Customers* table. Open the WebOrders table in Design view, make *CustID* the active field, and then create a lookup list to display values from another table using the following information:
   a. Display the *FirstName* and *LastName* fields from the *Customers* table.
   b. Sort the list in ascending order by the *LastName* field.
   c. Remove the check mark from the *Hide key column* check box.
   d. Store the *CustID* value.
   e. Accept the default label of *CustID* for the column.
5. Modify the Lookup property for the *CustID* field that will ensure only items within the list can be entered into the field.
6. Save the table, switch to Datasheet view, and then enter the following record to test the lookup list:

Web Order ID	10007
Customer ID	Select *106 Gary Gallagher* in the lookup list.
Date Ordered	Feb 26 2018

7. Print the datasheet.
8. Close the WebOrders table.

9

Assessment 2 Create a Table With a Multiple-Field Primary Key Field and Lookup Lists

1. With *2-ViewRite.accdb* open, create a new table using Design view to track the customers' purchases using the following information:

Field Name	Data Type	Field Size	Caption
WebOrdID	Short Text	5	Web Order ID
ProductID	Short Text	7	Product ID
Qty	Number	–	Quantity
Media	Short Text	11	–

2. A customer can choose to buy more than one TV series or season on the same order. When this occurs, the same order number is associated with more than one record in the table. Therefore, the primary key field cannot be based on the *WebOrdID* field alone. Assign a multiple-field primary key field using both the *WebOrdID* and *ProductID* fields. The combination of the order identification number and product identification number will uniquely describe each record in the table.
3. Save the table and name it *WebOrderDetails*.
4. Create a lookup list for the *WebOrdID* field that connects to the *WebOrdID* field in the WebOrders table. Add all three of the fields in the WebOrders table to the lookup list, do not specify a sort field, remove the check mark from the *Hide key column* check box, store *WebOrdID* in the field, and then accept the default field name. Modify the Lookup property to ensure only items within the list can be entered into the field.
5. Create a lookup list for the *ProductID* field that connects to the *ProductID* field in the TVSeries table. Add the *ProductID*, *Title*, and *SeasonNo* fields. Sort by *Title* and then by *SeasonNo*. Make sure the column is wide enough to display the entire title. Unhide the key column and then accept the default field name. Modify the Lookup property to ensure that only items within the list can be entered into the field.
6. Create a lookup list for the *Media* field that allows typing the desired values. The options include *DVD*, *Blu-ray*, *Download*, and *Multiformat*. Modify the Lookup property to ensure that only items within the list can be entered into the field.
7. Save the table and switch to Datasheet view. Add the following records to the WebOrderDetails datasheet to test the lookup lists:

Web Order ID	Product ID	Quantity	Media
10001	CV-1001 (Once Upon a Time)	1	Blu-ray
10001	CV-1022 (Criminal Minds)	1	DVD
10002	CV-1004 (The Big Bang Theory)	1	DVD
10003	CV-1016 (NCIS)	1	Multiformat
10003	CV-1017 (NCIS)	1	DVD
10003	CV-1018 (NCIS)	1	Download
10004	CV-1006 (Doctor Who)	1	DVD

8. Best fit the width of each column and print the datasheet.
9. Close the WebOrderDetails table. Click Yes when prompted to save changes to the layout.

Assessment 3 — Edit Relationships

1. With **2-ViewRite.accdb** open, open the Relationships window to view the relationships created by Access when the lookup lists were created.
2. Resize and move the table field list boxes to the approximate sizes and locations, as shown in Figure WB-2.1.
3. Edit the relationships as follows:
   a. Edit the one-to-many relationship between the Customers table and WebOrders table to activate referential integrity and the two cascade options.
   b. Edit the one-to-many relationship between the WebOrders table and WebOrderDetails table to activate referential integrity and the two cascade options.
   c. Edit the one-to-many relationship between the TVSeries table and WebOrderDetails table to activate referential integrity and the two cascade options.
4. Create and print a relationship report.
5. On your relationship report printout, write the type of relationship that exists between the WebOrders table and TVSeries table.
6. Close the relationship report for the **2-ViewRite** database. Click Yes to save the report and accept the default name in the Save As dialog box.
7. Close the Relationships window.

Figure WB-2.1 Assessment 3

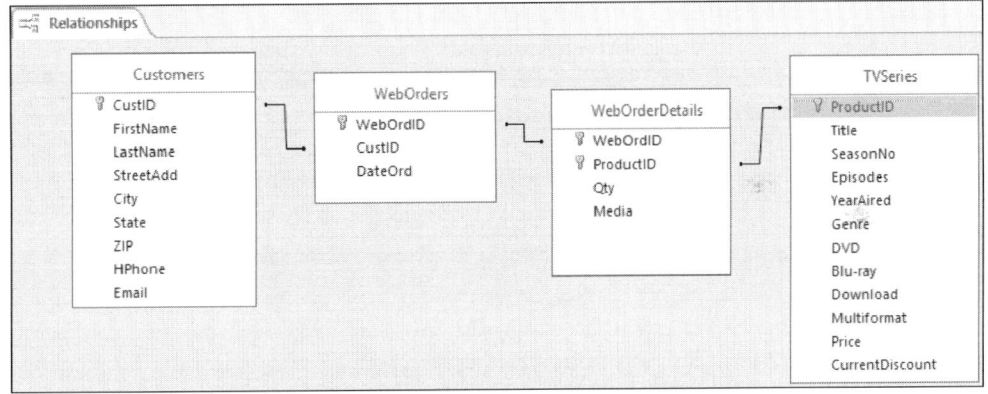

Assessment 4 — Create a Table with a One-to-One Relationship

1. With **2-ViewRite.accdb** open, create a new table using Design view to store a customer's credit card information using the following information:

Field Name	Data Type	Field Size	Caption
CustID	Short Text	3	Customer ID
CCType	Short Text	20	Credit Card Type
CCNumber	Short Text	16	Credit Card Number
CCExpMonth	Number	–	Expiry Month
CCExpYear	Number	–	Expiry Year

2. Make the *CustID* field the primary key field.
3. Save the table and name it *CustPymnt*.

4. Create a lookup list for the *CustID* field that connects to the *CustID* field in the Customers table. Include the *FirstName*, *LastName*, and *HPhone* fields. Sort the list by *LastName* and then by *FirstName*. Remove the check mark from the *Hide key column* check box. Accept all the other defaults. Modify the Lookup property to ensure that only items within the list can be entered into the field.
5. Save the table, switch to Datasheet view, and then enter the following record:

Customer ID	Select *106 Gary Gallagher* in the lookup list
Credit Card Type	Visa
Credit Card Number	0009100876453152
Expiry Month	7
Expiry Year	2020

6. Best fit the width of each column and then print the datasheet in landscape orientation.
7. Close the CustPymnt table. Click Yes when prompted to save changes to the layout.
8. Open the Relationships window and then open the Show Table dialog box.
9. Add the CustPymnt table to the window. Edit the one-to-one relationship between the Customers and CustPymnt tables to activate referential integrity and the two cascade options.
10. If necessary, rearrange the table field list boxes in the Relationships window so the join line between the CustPymnt and Customers tables can be seen more clearly.
11. Print a relationship report, changing page layout options as necessary to fit the report on one page. Close the relationship report. Click Yes to save the report and type *Relationships-A4* as the report name in the Save As dialog box.
12. Close the Relationships window.
13. Close **2-ViewRite.accdb**.

Visual Benchmark

Data Files

Create Lookup Lists and Edit Relationships

1. Open **2-PawsParadise.accdb**.
2. This database is similar to the Visual Benchmark database created in Chapter 1. However, an additional table has been created and several records have been added to the database. Spend a few moments becoming familiar with the tables and records.
3. Create the following lookup lists, making sure the field value saved is always the primary key field:
    a. In the Dogs table, look up the kennel category in the KennelCategories table. Make sure the *Hide key column* check box contains a check mark. Make sure the column is wide enough to display the entire category.
    b. In the Dogs table, look up the customer number in the DogOwners table. Remove the check mark from the *Hide key column* check box.
    c. In the Reservations table, look up the customer number in the DogOwners table. Remove the check mark from the *Hide key column* check box.
4. Open the Relationships window and edit the relationships to activate referential integrity and both cascade options for each relationship.
5. Rearrange and move the table field list boxes as necessary so that the Relationships window is similar to the one shown in Figure WB-2.2.
6. Create and print a relationship report.
7. Save the relationship report using the default name and then close the report and the Relationships window.
8. Close **2-PawsParadise.accdb**.

Figure WB-2.2 Visual Benchmark Relationships Window

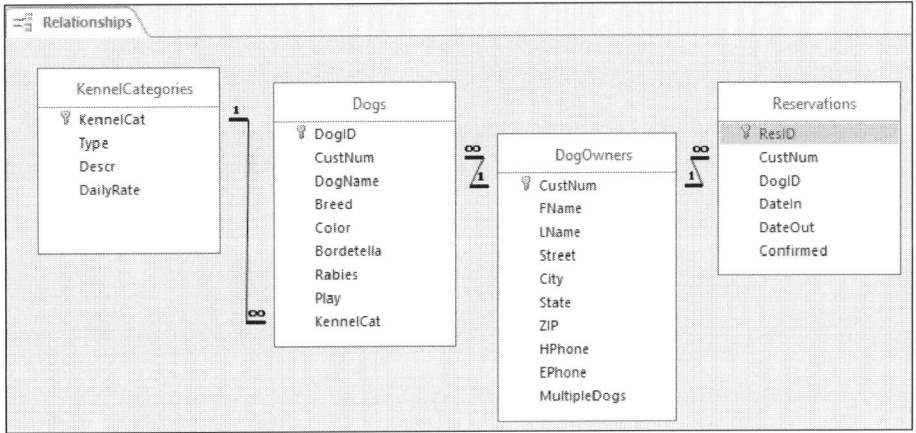

Case Study

Part 1

Data Files

You are working as an intern at Hillsdale Realty. The intern that worked there before you started developing a database for use in managing sales agents, listings, sales, and commission quotas. The previous intern did not have time to finish the database, however. Open **2-HillsdaleRealty.accdb** and enable the content. Open all the tables and review the fields and records to become familiar with the database.

The Agents table is not in first normal form. The field *AgentName* contains both the first and last names of each sales agent. To improve the table design, modify the table so two separate fields are used for sales agents' names. Add captions to the name fields. Correct the data in the datasheet so the names are correctly split into the two columns. Print the revised Agents table datasheet with all the column widths adjusted to best fit. Close the table.

Part 2

You decide to improve the efficiency of data entry by creating lookup lists as follows:

- In the Listings table, you want to be able to select the correct Agent ID by viewing the agent names in a sorted drop-down list. Display *AgentID* as the value in the field.
- In the Agents table, you want to be able to select the quota code by viewing all the quota codes and amounts in a drop-down list. Display the commission quota in the datasheet but store *QuotaID* as the field value. Edit the caption for the field to read *Quota* (instead of *Quota Code*).
- In the SalesAndComm table, you want to be able to select the correct listing number by viewing the listing numbers and addresses from the Listings table. Make sure the column width is wide enough to display all the street address information. Display *ListingNo* as the value in the field.

Open the Relationships window. If necessary, add all the tables to the window. Resize and arrange boxes so the join lines between tables are easy to follow and understand. Edit each relationship to activate referential integrity and the two cascade options. Create, print, and save a relationship report. Close the relationship report and then close the Relationships window.

Part 3

You have decided to add another table named *Preferences* to the database. Create the table using the information below. You determine the appropriate data types and other field properties.

Field Name	Lookup Lists
ClientID	–
ListingNo	Create a lookup list to the Listings table.
AgentID	Create a lookup list to the Agents table.
Preferences	Create a multiple-value list with the following items: Exclusive listing MLS listing Presale inspection Staging service

A client could have more than one listing at Hillsdale Realtors so you do not want to use the *ClientID* field as the primary key field. Create a composite key field using the two fields: *ClientID* and *ListingNo*. Add a sample record to the table to test the lookup lists and multiple-value field. Adjust all the column widths to best fit, print the datasheet, and then close the table, saving the layout. Open the Relationships window, add the new table, and then arrange the layout so that the join lines do not overlap. Edit the relationships between the Preferences, Listings, and Agents tables to activate referential integrity and the two cascade options. Create, print, and then save a new relationship report named *Relationships-Part3*.

Microsoft® Access®
Advanced Query Techniques

CHAPTER 3

> **Study Tools**

Study tools include a presentation and a list of chapter Quick Steps and Hint margin notes. Use these resources to help you further develop and review skills learned in this chapter.

> **Concepts Check**

Check your understanding by identifying application tools used in this chapter. If you are a SNAP user, launch the Concepts Check from your Assignments page.

> **Recheck**

Check your understanding by taking this quiz. If you are a SNAP user, launch the Recheck from your Assignments page.

Skills Exercise

Additional activities are available to SNAP users. If you are a SNAP user, access these activities from your Assignments page.

Skills Assessment

Assessment 1

Data Files

Extract Records Using a Filter and Prompted Queries

1. Open **3-ViewRite.accdb** and enable the content.
2. Open the Customers table.
3. Using the Filter By Form feature, display only those customers who reside in Burlington and have zip codes that begin with 05401. *Hint: Type* 05401* *in the* ZIP *field to specify only the first five characters in the ZIP code. The asterisk is a wildcard character that allows you to filter by specifying only a portion of the field value.*
4. Save the filter as a query named *CustBurlington05401*.
5. Close the Filter By Form datasheet and close the table. Click No when prompted to save changes to the table design.
6. Open the CustBurlington05401 query.
7. Adjust the column widths to Best Fit. Print the query results datasheet in landscape orientation with the left and right margins set to 0.5 inch and then close the query.
8. Create a new query in Design view using the following specifications:
   a. Add the tables WebOrderDetails, WebOrders, and TVSeries to the query.
   b. Add the fields *WebOrdID* (WebOrders table), *DateOrd*, *Qty*, *Title*, and *SeasonNo* to the query design grid.
   c. Create a parameter query to prompt the user to type the title of the TV series in the *Title* column. The prompt should be *Type the TV series title*.
   d. Save the query, name it *PromptedTVSeries*, and then close the query.
9. Run the PromptedTVSeries query. Type Modern Family at the Enter Parameter Value dialog box. Print the query results datasheet and then close the query.

15

10. Open the PromptedTVSeries query in Design view. Use Save As to name the query *PromptedOrderDates*. Delete the prompt message in the *Title* column. Create a parameter query to prompt the user to type the starting and ending dates for viewing web orders in the *DateOrd* column. The prompts should be *Type starting date* and *Type ending date*. Save and then close the query.
11. Run the PromptedOrderDates query. Type February 1, 2018 as the beginning date and February 28, 2018 as the ending date. Print the query results datasheet and then close the query.

Assessment 2 Modify Join Properties

1. With **3-ViewRite.accdb** open, create a new query in Design view using the following specifications:
   a. Add the Customers table and WebOrders table to the query.
   b. Add the fields *CustID*, *FirstName*, *LastName*, and *WebOrdID* to the query design grid. **Note: Add CustID *from the Customers table.***
   c. Modify the join type between the Customers table and WebOrders table to a left outer join.
   d. Save the query with the name *CustActivity*.
2. Run the query. Print the query results datasheet and then close the query.
3. Create a new query in Design view using the following specifications:
   a. Add the WebOrderDetails table and TVSeries table to the query.
   b. Add the fields *WebOrdID*, *ProdID*, *Title*, and *SeasonNo* to the query design grid. **Note: Add ProdID *from the TVSeries table*.**
   c. Modify the join type between the TVSeries table and WebOrderDetails table to a left outer join.
   d. Save the query with the name *AllTVSeries*.
4. Run the query. Print the query results datasheet and then close the query.

Assessment 3 Create a Query and Subquery to Perform Calculations and Use a Logical Function

1. With **3-ViewRite.accdb** open, open the CustActivity query in Design view, use Save As to name the new query *TotalWithDiscount*, and then modify the query as follows:
   a. Modify the join type between the Customers table and WebOrders table to an inner join.
   b. Add the WebOrderDetails table and TVSeries table to the query.
   c. Add the fields *DateOrd*, *Qty*, *Title*, *SeasonNo*, and *Price* to the query design grid.
   d. Delete the *FirstName* and *LastName* fields from the query.
   e. Create a calculated field with the column label *DiscountPrice* that subtracts the *Price* times the *CurrentDiscount* from the *Price*. Change the caption to *Discount Price*.
   f. Use a logical function to add the *Total* field. If the *CurrentDiscount* is greater than zero, then take the *Qty* times the *DiscountPrice*. If this is false, then take the *Qty* times the *Price*.
2. Save and then run the query. Adjust the column widths to Best Fit. Print the query results datasheet in landscape orientation with the left and right margins set to 0.5 inch and then close the query.
3. Create a new query in Design view that calculates the total sale with tax as follows:
   a. Nest the TotalWithDiscount query in the new query.
   b. Add the fields *WebOrdID*, *DateOrd*, and *Total* to the query design grid.

c. Create a calculated field with the column label *Tax* that multiples the value in the *Total* column times 0.06 (the decimal equivalent of 6%). Format the calculated column by applying the Standard format.

d. Create a second calculated column with the column label *TotalSaleWithTax* that adds the *Total* column to the *Tax* column. Change the caption to *Total Sale With Tax*.

e. Save the query with the name *SalesWithTotalAndTax*.

4. Run the query. Adjust the column widths to Best Fit. Print the query results datasheet. Close the query, saving the changes.

Assessment 4 Use Action Queries to Archive Records and Update Selling Prices

1. With **3-ViewRite.accdb** open, open the TotalWithDiscount query in Design view, use Save As to name the new query *Feb2018SalesMakeTable*, and then modify the query as follows:
   a. Use the *Between* expression to add a criterion to select the records for sales during the month of February 2018.
   b. Run the query to make sure the correct records are being selected.
   c. Change the query to a make-table query, name the new table *Feb2018WebSales*, and archive the table in the current database.
   d. Save, run, and then close the query.

2. Open the Feb2018WebSales table. Best Fit the column widths and then print the datasheet. Close the table, saving the changes to the layout.

3. Open the Feb2018SalesMakeTable query in Design view, use Save As to name the new query *Feb2018SalesDelete*, and then modify the query as follows:
   a. Change the query to a delete query.
   b. Delete the *DiscountPrice* and *Total* columns from the query design grid. Remove the Customers, WebOrderDetails, and TVSeries tables from the query.
   c. Save the query, run the query, and then close the query window.

4. Open the TotalWithDiscount query. Best Fit the column widths and then print the query results datasheet in landscape orientation with the left and right margins set to 0.5 inch and then close the query.

5. Create a new query in Design view to update the selling prices of TVSeries with product IDs from CV-1020 to CV-1022 as follows:
   a. Add the TVSeries table to the query.
   b. Add the *ProdID* and *Price* fields to the query design grid.
   c. Change the query to an update query and add a formula that will add $1.05 to the selling price of each series that has a product ID from CV-1020 to CV-1022.
   d. Save the query with the name *PriceUpdate*.
   e. Run the query and then close the query window.

6. Open the TVSeries table. Adjust the column widths to Best Fit and hide the *Current Discount* column. Print the datasheet in landscape orientation with the left and right margins set to 0.25 inch. and then close the table.

7. Close **3-ViewRite.accdb**.

Visual Benchmark

Data Files

Calculate Days Boarded and Amount Due Using Nested Queries

1. Open **3-PawsParadise.accdb**.
2. Review the query results datasheet shown in Figure WB-3.1. This query is the result of nesting a query within a query. Create the calculations as follows:
   a. Create the first query to calculate the number of days a dog is boarded in the kennel. Show in the query results the reservation ID, the customer's name, the dog's name, and the two date fields. Calculate the number of days the dog was boarded. Save the query with the name *DaysBoarded*.
   b. Nest the DaysBoarded query in a new query. Add the Dogs and KennelCategories tables to the query. Join the DaysBoarded query to the Dogs table on the common *DogName* field. Add the fields to the query design grid, as shown in Figure WB-3.1, and then calculate the amount due for each reservation.
   c. Sort and format the query results as shown in the figure. The font used is Arial Narrow and the font size is 11 points. The alternate row color used is Maroon 1 (from the *Standard Colors* section of the color palette). *Note: The first row is not formatted differently from the remainder of the datasheet; the row displays with a different color because the first row is selected.* Save the query with the name *ReservationTotals*.
3. Print the ReservationTotals query results datasheet in landscape orientation with the left and right margins set to 0.5 inch.
4. Close the query.
5. Close **3-PawsParadise.accdb**.

Figure WB-3.1 Visual Benchmark

Reservation	First Name	Last Name	Dog's Name	Date In	Date Out	Days Boarded	Kennel Type	Daily Rate	Amount Due
1	Shawn	Jenkins	Abby	11/9/2018	11/12/2018	3	V.I.P. Suite	$48.50	$145.50
2	Shawn	Jenkins	Winnie	11/9/2018	11/12/2018	3	V.I.P. Suite	$48.50	$145.50
3	Sean	Gallagher	Tank	11/10/2018	11/13/2018	3	V.I.P. Suite	$48.50	$145.50
4	Sofia	Ramos	Apollo	11/11/2018	11/18/2018	7	Indoor/Outdoor Suite	$35.50	$248.50
5	Sofia	Ramos	Murphy	11/11/2018	11/18/2018	7	Indoor/Outdoor Suite	$35.50	$248.50
6	Dina	Lombardi	Niko	11/12/2018	11/16/2018	4	Indoor/Outdoor Suite	$35.50	$142.00
7	Natale	Rizzo	Dallas	11/12/2018	11/14/2018	2	Indoor/Outdoor Suite	$35.50	$71.00
8	James	Chung	Lassie	11/12/2018	11/13/2018	1	Deluxe Suite	$39.50	$39.50
9	Bernard	Jedicke	Kosmo	11/12/2018	11/13/2018	1	Day Care Boarding	$18.50	$18.50
10	Bernard	Jedicke	Sierra	11/12/2018	11/13/2018	1	Day Care Boarding	$18.50	$18.50
11	Bernard	Jedicke	Emma	11/12/2018	11/13/2018	1	Day Care Boarding	$18.50	$18.50
12	Carlotta	Sanchez	Scrappy	11/13/2018	11/19/2018	6	Deluxe Suite	$39.50	$237.00
13	Michael	Mancini	Harley	11/13/2018	11/23/2018	10	Indoor/Outdoor Suite	$35.50	$355.00
14	Glen	Waters	Barney	11/14/2018	11/29/2018	15	Indoor/Outdoor Suite	$35.50	$532.50
15	Lenora	Diaz	Zack	11/14/2018	11/17/2018	3	Indoor/Outdoor Suite	$35.50	$106.50
16	Maeve	Murphy	King	11/15/2018	11/19/2018	4	V.I.P. Suite	$48.50	$194.00
17	Valerie	McTague	Chloe	11/16/2018	11/19/2018	3	Deluxe Suite	$39.50	$118.50
18	Nadia	Costa	Bailey	11/17/2018	11/24/2018	7	Deluxe Suite	$39.50	$276.50
19	Juan	Torres	Taffy	11/17/2018	11/21/2018	4	V.I.P. Suite	$48.50	$194.00
20	Liam	Doherty	Zeus	11/18/2018	11/23/2018	5	V.I.P. Suite	$48.50	$242.50
21	Dillon	Farrell	Chico	11/18/2018	11/22/2018	4	Indoor/Outdoor Suite	$35.50	$142.00
22	Diane	Ye	Elvis	11/20/2018	11/25/2018	5	Indoor/Outdoor Suite	$35.50	$177.50
23	Lorenzo	Rivera	Fifi	11/22/2018	11/27/2018	5	V.I.P. Suite	$48.50	$242.50
24	Lorenzo	Rivera	Lucky	11/22/2018	11/27/2018	5	Indoor/Outdoor Suite	$35.50	$177.50
25	Bernard	Jedicke	Kosmo	11/26/2018	11/27/2018	1	Day Care Boarding	$18.50	$18.50
26	Bernard	Jedicke	Sierra	11/26/2018	11/27/2018	1	Day Care Boarding	$18.50	$18.50
27	Bernard	Jedicke	Emma	11/26/2018	11/27/2018	1	Day Care Boarding	$18.50	$18.50

Case Study

Part 1 — Data Files

You are continuing your work as an intern at Hillsdale Realty. The office manager has asked you to provide a series of printouts with information from the database. Open **3-HillsdaleRealty.accdb** and enable the content. Design, create, save, run, and print query results to provide the required information. You determine the proper page setup to print each query on one page and an appropriate descriptive name for each query.

- Produce a list of sales by agent that includes the date of sale, address, sale price, and commission rate for each sale. Sort the query results by the agent's last name and then by date of sale, sorting both fields in ascending order.
- Modify the first query to allow the office manager to type the agent's name when she runs the query; this will allow viewing individual sales reports by agent. To test the query, run it using the agent name *Cecilia Ortega*. Save the revised query using a new name.
- Produce a list that shows each agent and his or her clients. Show the client ID, client first name, and client last name next to the agent's name. The manager wants to see which agents have not yet signed any clients, so you need to make sure the query results show all the agents.
- Produce a list of agents that shows each agent's co-broker agent. The Agents table contains a field named *CoBroker*. This field is the agent ID for the person assigned to a co-broker listing. The office manager has requested a list that shows the agent's last name, instead of his or her ID number, in the *CoBroker* field. Sort the list in ascending order by AgentLName. ***Hint: Create a self-join query and remember to use the alias and caption properties to rename the table and the column that will display the co-broker agent last name.***
- Modify the first query to add a column to calculate the amount of commission that will be owed on the sale by multiplying the sale price times the commission rate. Save the revised query using a new name.
- Use a query to update all the commission quota values to add 15%. After updating the values, create a new query to show each agent and his or her respective commission quota. Sort the list in ascending order by agent last name.

Part 2

The office manager at Hillsdale Realty would like to see the five highest sale prices to date. Research in Help how to create a top-values query using the *Return* option box in the Query Setup group. Using the information you learned in Help, modify the first query created in Part 1 to produce the top-five list. Save the revised query using a new name and print the query results on one page. ***Hint: Remove the sorting from the original query and then sort by sale price in descending order before converting the query to a top-five values query.***

Part 3

The office manager at Hillsdale Realty would like to review the client preferences for each listing and have each preference display on a separate line. Include in the list the listing date, street address, client's name, and client's telephone number. Add criteria to select only those records for cases in which the client has requested a presale inspection or staging service for his or her listing. Save and print the query on one page.

Microsoft® Access®
Creating and Using Custom Forms

CHAPTER 4

Study Tools

Study tools include a presentation and a list of chapter Quick Steps and Hint margin notes. Use these resources to help you further develop and review skills learned in this chapter.

Concepts Check

Check your understanding by identifying application tools used in this chapter. If you are a SNAP user, launch the Concepts Check from your Assignments page.

Recheck

Check your understanding by taking this quiz. If you are a SNAP user, launch the Recheck from your Assignments page.

Skills Exercise

Additional activities are available to SNAP users. If you are a SNAP user, access these activities from your Assignments page.

Skills Assessment

Assessment 1

Data Files

Create a Custom Form Using Design View

1. Open **4-ViewRite.accdb** and enable the content.
2. Create a query named *CustWebOrders* using the following specifications:
   a. Add the WebOrderDetails, WebOrders, and TVSeries tables to the query.
   b. Add the following fields first from the WebOrders table, then from the WebOrderDetails table, and then from the TVSeries table:

WebOrders Table	**WebOrderDetails Table**	**TVSeries Table**
WebOrdID	Qty	Title
CustID		Price
DateOrd		

   c. Run the query, save the query, and then close the query results datasheet.
3. Create a new form called *WebCustOrders* using Design view and then build the form using the following specifications:
   a. Expand the width of the form in the grid to the 6.5-inch position on the horizontal ruler.
   b. Add a title control object in the *Form Header* section and then type the text Web Customer Orders. Use the move handle at the top left of the selected title control object to move the title until the first letter (*W*) is at approximately the 1.5-inch position on the horizontal ruler.
   c. Add your name in a label control object centered in the *Form Footer* section.
   d. Apply the Retrospect theme.

21

e. Connect the Customers table to the form and add all the fields to the *Detail* section in the layout shown in Figure WB-4.1. Adjust the widths of the control objects as shown. Remember to use the Size/Space button and Align button to position multiple control objects at the same horizontal or vertical position and adjust spacing between control objects.

Figure WB-4.1 Assessment 1

f. Change the tab order of the fields so the *Phone* field is selected after the *CustID* field and the *Email* field is selected after the *LastName* field.
g. Add a tab control object below the existing fields with a height of approximately 2 inches and a width that extends to the right edge of the form according to these specifications:
   1) On the first page, change the caption to *Web Orders* and add all the fields from the CustWebOrders query in a subform. Delete the subform label control object. Delete the label control object and text box control object for the *CustID* field in the subform and then move the remaining fields up to fill the space. Move and resize the subform to be 6 inches. Best fit the column widths in Form view to allow viewing all the columns on the page.
   2) On the second page, change the caption to *Payment Information* and add all the fields except *CustID* from the CustPymnt table in a subform. Delete the subform label control object and move and resize the subform to be 6 inches. If necessary, resize the main form to be 6.5 inches. Best fit the column widths in Form view to allow viewing all the columns on the page.
4. In the main form, apply bold formatting to the label control objects and the Green, Accent 6, Lighter 80% (last column, second row in the *Theme Colors* section) background color to the text box control objects.
5. Save the form.
6. Print the form in Form view with the first record displayed and the Web Orders page active.
7. Close the form.

Assessment 2

Create a Form Using the Form Wizard and Add a Calculation and Graphics

Data Files

1. With **4-ViewRite.accdb** open, create a new form using the Form Wizard as follows:
   a. Select all the fields from the TVSeries table.
   b. Apply the Columnar format.
   c. Accept the default form name *TVSeries*.
2. View the completed form in Form view.
3. Switch to Design view and edit the form to resemble the one shown in Figure WB-4.2 using the following additional information:
   a. The *Amount of Discount* field is a calculated field that uses a formula to multiply the price by the current discount. Apply the Currency format to the result.
   b. Find the online image by searching using the keyword *TV*. Choose a suitable alternative image if the image shown is not available on the computer you are using. The image (**MStudentFile.png**) may also be accessed from the student data files.
   c. For the title text and lines, apply the Maroon 5 color (available in the *Standard Colors* section).
   d. Use your best judgment in applying other formatting options to match the form in Figure WB-4.2 as closely as possible.
4. Print the form in Form view with the first record displayed.
5. Save and close the form.

Figure WB-4.2 Assessment 2

Assessment 3

Create a Restricted-Use Form

1. With **4-ViewRite.accdb** open, create a Datasheet form using the CustPymnt table.
2. Modify the form so users cannot delete records.
3. Display the form in Datasheet view with the Home tab active and a record selected.
4. Using the Insert Screenshot command or Print Screen key with the Paste feature, insert a screenshot of the screen with the Delete button dimmed while the record is selected.
5. Paste the screenshot into a blank Word document. Below the screenshot, type your name, the chapter number, the assessment number, and any other identification information required by your instructor.
6. Print the document.
7. Save the Word document and name it **4-ViewRiteForm**.
8. Exit Word.
9. Save the form using the default form name *CustPymnt* and then close the form.

Assessment 4

Create a Custom Form Using the Blank Form Tool and Add a List Box

1. With **4-ViewRite.accdb** open, create a new form using the Blank Form tool that adds all the fields from the Customers table. Increase the width of the labels column so all the label text is visible in the form.
2. Add a list box control object between the *City* field and *State* field. Type the values into the list as follows:

    Burlington
    Charlotte
    Colchester

    Store the values in the field named *City* and accept the default label for the control object at the last List Box Wizard dialog box.
3. Delete the label control object for the list box.
4. Add this title to the form: *Customer Maintenance Form*. Resize the title control object to fit the text. Add your name in a label control object centered in the *Form Footer* section.
5. Save the form with the name *CustomerMaintenance*.
6. Switch to Form view and then add the following new record to the Customers table:

Customer ID	121
First Name	Morgan
Last Name	Kalil
Street Address	29011 Greenbush Road
City	(Click *Charlotte* in the list box.)
State	(Accept the default value of *VT*.)
ZIP Code	05445-9314
Phone	802-555-9185
Email	m.kalil@emcp.net

7. Print the selected record for the new customer and then close the form.
8. Close **4-ViewRite.accdb**.

Visual Benchmark

Create a Custom Reservations Form

Data Files

1. Open **4-PawsParadise.accdb**.
2. Review the form shown in Figure WB-4.3 and Figure WB-4.4. This form was created from scratch in Design view. Create the form using your best judgment for alignment, spacing, sizing, and positioning of controls and follow these specifications:
    a. Connect the Reservations table to the main form.
    b. Apply the Ion Boardroom theme.
    c. Apply the Dark Blue line color and set the line thickness to 3 points.
    d. The days boarded value is calculated by subtracting the two date fields.
    e. The Default View property (Format tab) for each subform was changed from Datasheet to Single Form. This view displays the fields one below the other instead of in a tabular arrangement. *Hint: Create the subform by including the linked common field in the Subform Wizard dialog box so that the correct relationship between the main form and subform is established. Then delete the extra control objects while editing the subform object.*
3. Save the form, naming it *Reservations*.
4. Display the form in Form view and then print the first record.
5. Close the form and then close **4-PawsParadise.accdb**.

Figure WB-4.3 Visual Benchmark Custom Form with Dog Information Tab Displayed

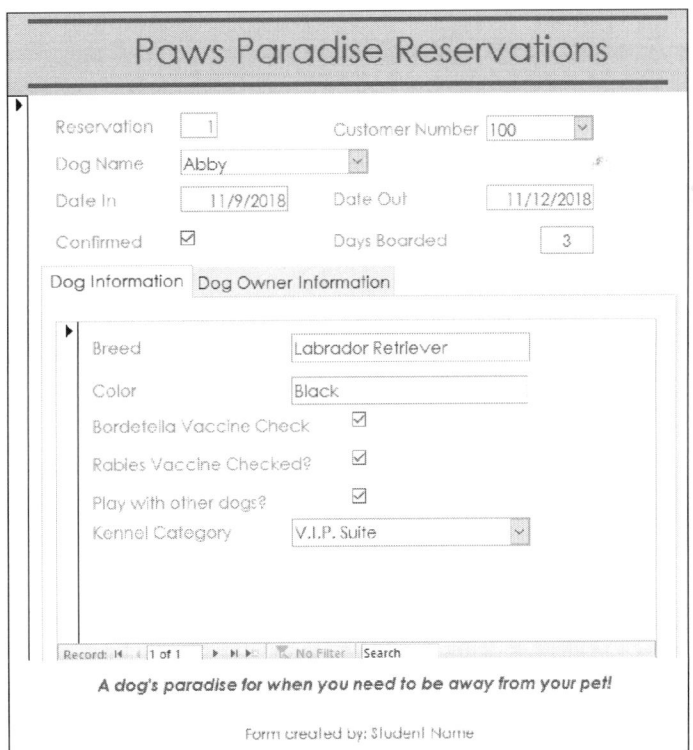

Figure WB-4.4 Visual Benchmark Custom Form with Dog Owner Information Tab Displayed

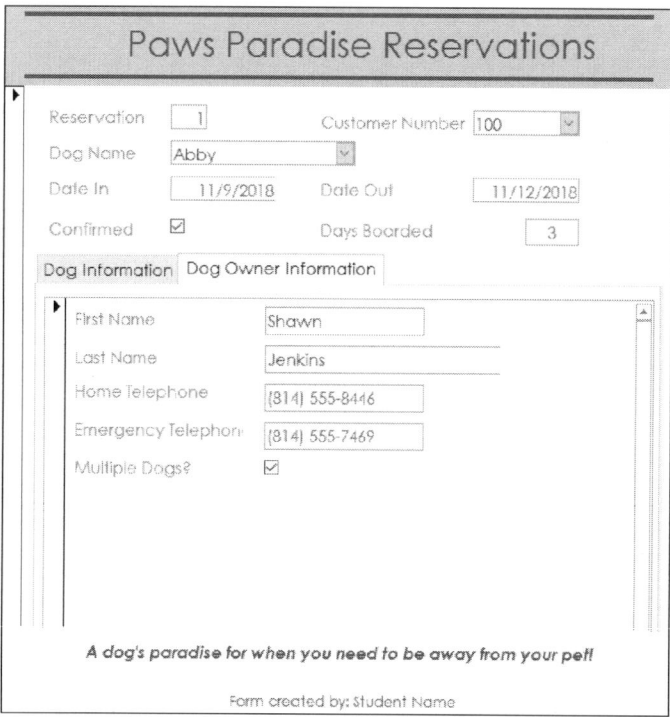

Case Study

Part 1

Data Files

You are continuing your work as an intern with Hillsdale Realty. The office manager has asked you to create a form for easier data entry and maintenance of listings and sales information. Open **4-HillsdaleRealty.accdb** and enable the content. Design and create a form similar to the one shown in Figure WB-4.5 using the Listings table and SalesAndComm table. Apply the Organic theme and Orange colors. Include the calculated field at the bottom of the subform. Do not stop at any calculated fields and modify the tab order of the fields to match the arrangement of the fields in Figure WB-4.5. *Hints: Change the default view for the subform to Single Form and add a calculated control in the subform control object that multiplies the sale price times the commission rate. Search for the online image using the keywords* for sale; *choose another suitable image if the one shown is not available on the computer you are using.* The image (**SStudentFile.png**) may also be accessed from the student data files. Save the form with an appropriate name. Print the first record in the form.

Part 2

The office manager at Hillsdale Realty would like to have another form that displays the information from the Agents table along with the clients related to each agent. Design and create this form. You determine the form design, layout, and formatting. Save the form with an appropriate name. Print the form with the first record displayed in the main form.

Figure WB-4.5 Case Study Part 1

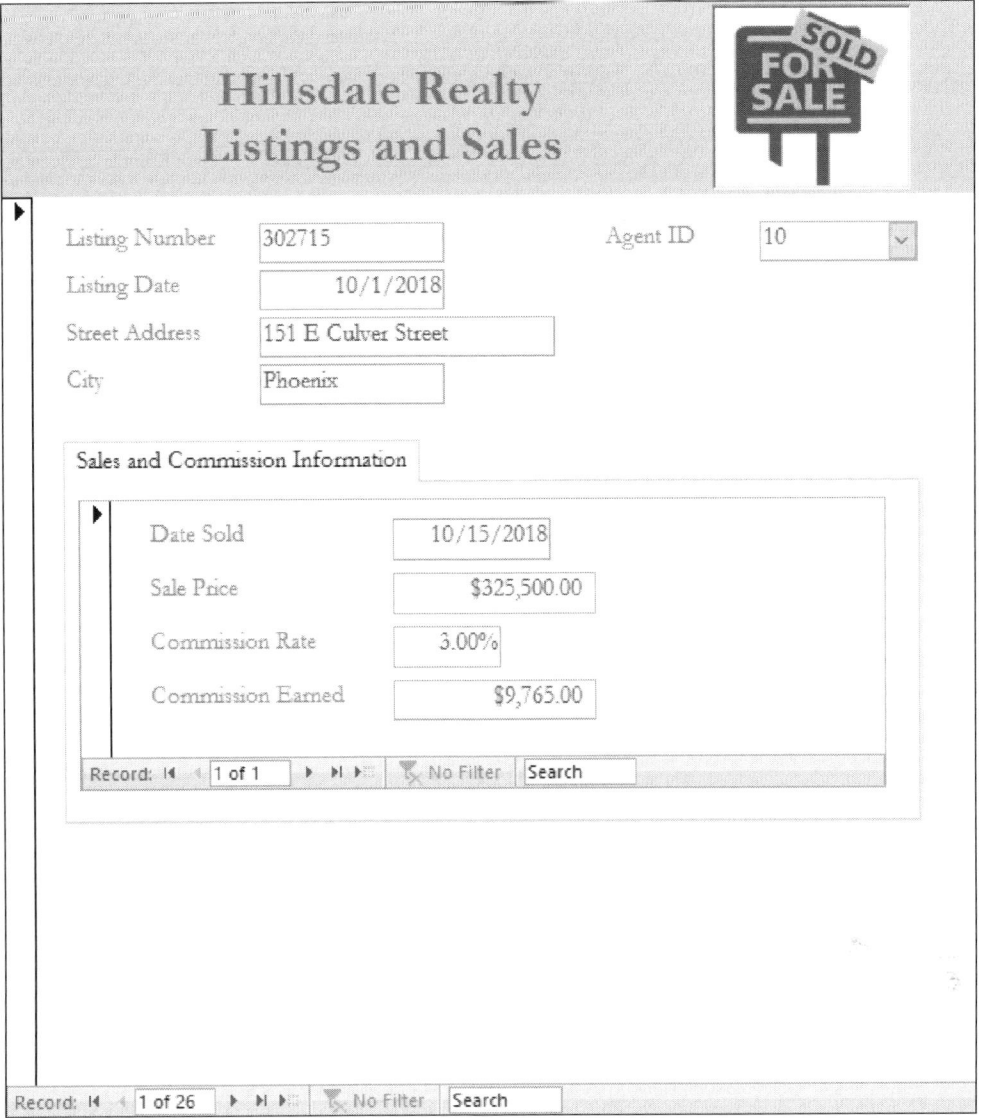

Part 3

Open the main form created for Hillsdale Realty in Part 1. While viewing the form, you realize that the Record Navigation bar at the bottom of the subform is not needed since a listing will have only one sale record. Remove the Record Navigation bar in the subform by opening the subform's Property Sheet task pane. At the Format tab, change the Navigation Buttons property to *No*. Close the Property Sheet task pane and then display the form in Form view. Notice that the subform no longer displays a Record Navigation bar. Save the revised form. Take a screenshot of the revised form using the Insert Screenshot command or Print Screen key with the Paste feature. Paste the screenshot into a new Word document. Below the screenshot, type your name, the chapter number, and any other identifying information required by your instructor. Print the Word document. Save the Word document as **4-HillsdaleRealty** and then exit Word.

Microsoft® Access® Level 2

Unit 1 Performance Assessment

Data Files

Before beginning unit work, copy the AL2U1 folder to your storage medium and then make AL2U1 the active folder.

Assessing Proficiency

In this unit, you have learned to design advanced tables that incorporate the best practices in database design. You created tables with multiple-field primary keys, multiple-value fields, attachment fields, and lookup fields to retrieve data from another table. You learned to modify the join type in a relationship to achieve various query results and to understand the concept of normalization as it applies to table design. Select queries, parameter queries, and action queries were created. Finally, Design view was used to build a custom form that includes calculations, multiple pages, and subforms.

Assessment 1

Create Tables for a Property Management Database

1. Create a new database named **U1-BenchmarkPropMgt.accdb**.
2. Create the tables shown in Figure WB-U1.1 to store residential building management and tenant information; set the primary key field and assign data types and field sizes. Leave field sizes at the default setting for those fields that a field size has not been specified in Figure WB-U1.1.
3. Close any tables that have been left open.
4. Open the Access Options dialog box and then click the *Compact on Close* check box with the Current Database pane active to make sure the file size is optimized each time the database is closed. Click OK at the message stating that the current database must be closed and reopened for the option to take effect.
5. Close **U1-BenchmarkPropMgt.accdb**.

Figure WB-U1.1 Assessment 1

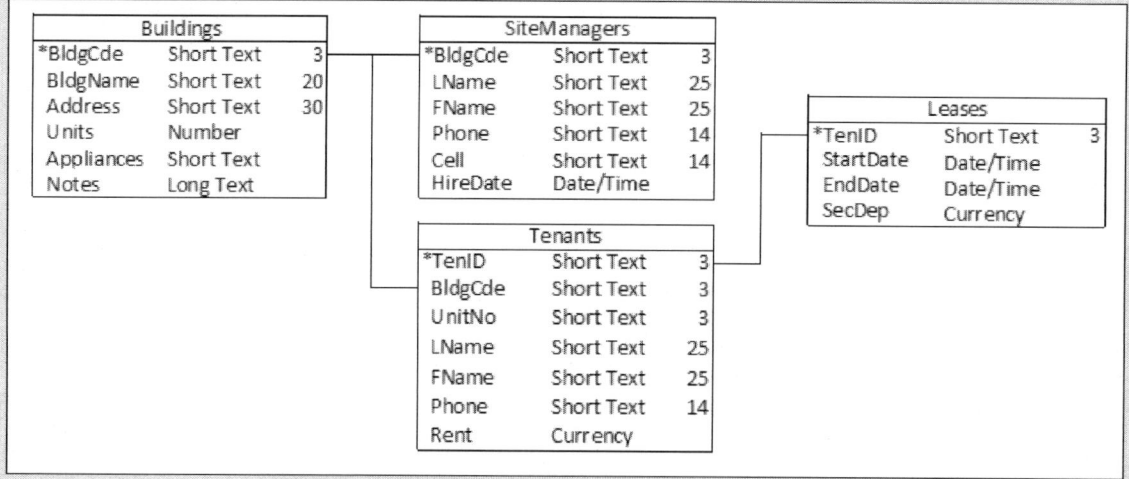

Assessment 2

Add Captions and Modify Field Properties

1. Open **U1-BenchmarkPropMgt.accdb** and then create captions for the fields as follows:

   Buildings Table

Field Name	Caption
BldgCde	Bldg Code
BldgName	Name

   Leases Table

Field Name	Caption
TenID	Tenant ID
StartDate	Start Date
EndDate	End Date
SecDep	Security Deposit

   SiteManagers Table

Field Name	Caption
BldgCde	Bldg Code
LName	Last Name
FName	First Name
Phone	Telephone
Cell	Cell Phone
HireDate	Hire Date

   Tenants Table

Field Name	Caption
TenID	Tenant ID
BldgCde	Bldg Code
UnitNo	Unit No
LName	Last Name
FName	First Name
Phone	Telephone

2. Make *UnitNo* in the Tenants table a required field; disallow the use of zero-length strings.
3. Create a custom format for all the date fields that displays dates in the short date format, with leading zeros for months and days. Use slashes (/) to separate the sections in the date—for example, *01/05/2018*.

4. Create the following custom input masks:
    a. For the *BldgCde* field in the Buildings table, require three digits and display an underscore character as the placeholder. Do not store the display characters.
    b. For the *TenID* field in the Tenants table, require three letters or digits and display an underscore character as the placeholder. Do not store the display characters.
    c. In each date field, create an input mask that will require dates to be entered using the short date format created in Step 3 and requiring all digits. Do not store the display characters. *Hint: Use the Input Mask Wizard to create the first input mask, modify the code created by the wizard to change optional digits to required digits, and then copy and paste the input mask codes to the other two date fields.*
    d. Require that all the telephone numbers include the area code and that hyphens are used between sections of the number. Display the pound symbol (#) as the placeholder character. (See the hint provided for Step 4c.) Do not store the display characters.
5. Enable rich text formatting in the *Notes* field in the Buildings table.
6. Make *1,250.00* the default value in the *Rent* field in the Tenants table.
7. Save and then close all the tables.

Assessment 3

Add Records

1. With **U1-BenchmarkPropMgt.accdb** open, add the following records:

    Buildings Table

Field	Record 1	Record 2	Record 3
Bldg Code	115	120	125
Name	Coventry Park	Mornington Place	Bayview Towers
Address	33 Westview Road	1100 Forrester Lane	12 Lakeview Circle
Units	38	60	110
Appliances	(leave blank)	(leave blank)	(leave blank)
Notes	New roof in 2018	Furnace and air conditioning units under warranty until 2021	Parking lot resurfaced in 2015

    Leases Table

Field	Record 1	Record 2	Record 3
Tenant ID	C01	C02	C03
Start Date	01 01 2018	02 01 2018	02 01 2018
End Date	12 31 2018	01 31 2019	01 31 2019
Security Deposit	1250	1250	1325

    SiteManagers Table

Field	Record 1	Record 2	Record 3
Bldg Code	115	120	125
Last Name	Jenkins	Hernandez	Doxtator
First Name	Blair	Maria	Cody
Telephone	800 555 3485	800 555 8675	800 555 9677
Cell Phone	800 555 3748	800 555 3996	800 555 7795
Hire Date	02 08 2015	04 23 2013	09 15 2014

Tenants Table

Field	Record 1	Record 2	Record 3
Tenant ID	C01	C02	C03
Bldg Code	115	115	115
Unit No	110	215	320
Last Name	Chen	Ayoub	Reiser
First Name	Wei	Mona	Helena
Telephone	519 555 8776	519 555 2286	519 555 7668
Rent	1250	1250	1325

2. Apply bold formatting and the red font color to the years entered in the *Notes* field in each record of the Buildings table.
3. For each table, adjust the column widths until all the data is entirely visible. Print each table, adjusting the print options as necessary to fit each table on one page.
4. Save and then close all the tables.

Assessment 4

Create Lookup Lists and Edit Relationships

1. With **U1-BenchmarkPropMgt.accdb** open, create the following lookup lists to display values from another table:
   a. In the SiteManagers table, create a lookup field for the *BldgCde* field that displays the building codes and names from the Buildings table. Sort the list by building name and show the key column. Widen the column that displays the building names to accommodate longer names that may be added to the table. Store the *BldgCde* value in the field.
   b. In the Tenants table, create a lookup field for the *BldgCde* field using the same specifications as for Step 1a.
   c. In the Leases table, create a lookup field for the *TenID* field that displays the tenant IDs, first names, and last names from the Tenants table. Sort the list by last name and show the key column. Store the *TenID* value in the field.
2. Create a multiple-value lookup field for the *Appliances* field in the Buildings table that contains the following items:

    Refrigerator
    Stove
    Microwave
    Dishwasher
    Washer
    Dryer

3. Edit the three records to populate the *Appliances* field as follows:

Bldg Code	Appliances
115	Refrigerator, Stove, Microwave
120	Refrigerator, Stove, Microwave, Dishwasher
125	Refrigerator, Stove, Dishwasher, Washer, Dryer

4. Adjust the field width of the *Appliances* column to best fit, change the width of the *Notes* column to 35 characters, and then change the row height to 30 points. Print the Buildings table in landscape orientation with the left and right margins set to 0.25 inch.
5. Close the Buildings table, saving changes to the table layout.
6. Open the Relationships window. Edit all the relationships to turn on referential integrity and the two cascade options.
7. Arrange the table field list boxes in the window to show the relationships with the primary tables on the left and the related tables on the right. Make sure no join lines overlap so that each relationship is clearly distinguished from the others. Create, save, and then print a relationship report using the default report name.
8. Close the relationship report window and Relationships window.

Assessment 5

Create Select Queries

1. With **U1-BenchmarkPropMgt.accdb** open, design and create the following select queries:
   a. A PromptedTenant query that displays the *BldgCde* and *BldgName* fields from the Buildings table and the *UnitNo*, *FName*, *LName*, and *Phone* fields from the Tenants table. Include prompts to specify the building code and unit number criteria when the query is run.
   b. A PromptedLease query that displays the *TenID* from the Tenants table; the *BldgName* from the Buildings table; the *UnitNo*, *FName*, and *LName* fields from the Tenants table; and the *StartDate*, *EndDate*, and *SecDep* fields from the Leases table. Include prompts to specify the starting date and ending date criteria when the query is run.
   c. A TenantsList query that displays the *BldgCde* and *BldgName* fields from the Buildings table and the *UnitNo*, *FName*, *LName*, and *Rent* fields from the Tenants table. Sort in ascending order by building name. Modify the join properties to show all the records from the Buildings table in a left outer join.
   d. A BuildingsList query that displays all the fields in the Buildings table except the *Notes* field. Show each entry in the multiple-value *Appliances* field in a separate row in the query results datasheet and assign the field the caption *Supplied Appliances*.
2. Run the PromptedTenant query. Type 115 when prompted for the building code and 110 when prompted for the unit number. Print the query results datasheet and then close the query.
3. Run the PromptedLease query. Type 02/01/2018 when prompted for the starting date and 01/31/2019 when prompted for the ending date. Print the query results datasheet in landscape orientation and then close the query.
4. Run the TenantsList query, print the query results datasheet, and then close the query.
5. Run the BuildingsList query, print the query results datasheet in landscape orientation, and then close the query.

Assessment 6 — Calculate in a Query and Use an Update Query to Increase Rents

1. With **U1-BenchmarkPropMgt.accdb** open, create a query to calculate the total rental income from each unit as follows:
   a. Open the TenantsList query in Design view and use Save Object As to name the query *RentalIncome*.
   b. Modify the join properties to show records only when the joined fields are equal in both tables using an inner join.
   c. Add a calculated field to the query with the column heading *AnnualRent* that calculates 12 months of rental income. Change the caption to *Annual Rent*.
   d. Run the query and add a *Total* row in the query results datasheet with a Sum function in the *Rent* and *Annual Rent* columns.
   e. Print the query results datasheet in landscape orientation and then close the query, saving the changes.
2. Create an update query named *RentIncrease* to increase all the rents by 4%. Run the query.
3. Close the RentIncrease query.
4. Open the RentalIncome query, print the query results datasheet in landscape orientation, and then close the query.

Assessment 7 — Design and Create Forms

Data Files

1. With **U1-BenchmarkPropMgt.accdb** open, design and create a form to enter data into the Tenants table as a main form with the Leases table in a subform, similar to the one shown in Figure WB-U1.2. Name the form *TenantsAndLeases*. Modify the tab order to move in this sequence: *Tenant ID*, *Bldg Code*, *Unit No*, *Telephone*, *First Name*, *Last Name*, and *Rent*. Remove the tab stop from *Annual Rent*, as it is a calculated control. Use your best judgment to match the color formatting with the theme colors. Add labels and graphics as shown. The image (**BStudentFile.jpg**) may also be accessed from the student data files. (Note that the subform does not show a Record Navigation bar. Refer to Chapter 4, Case Study Part 3 if you need help turning off the bar.)
2. Print all the records using the TenantsAndLeases form and then close the form, saving the changes.
3. Design and create a form to enter data into the Buildings table as a main form with the SiteManagers table in a subform. Name the main form *BldgsAndMgrs*. You determine the form design, layout, and formatting. Include an appropriate online picture in the form. The image (**BStudentFile.jpg**) may also be accessed from the student data files. Add your name in the *Form Footer* section. Print the first record in the Buildings table displayed in Form view.
4. Close **U1-BenchmarkPropMgt.accdb**.

Figure WB-U1.2 Assessment 7, Step 1

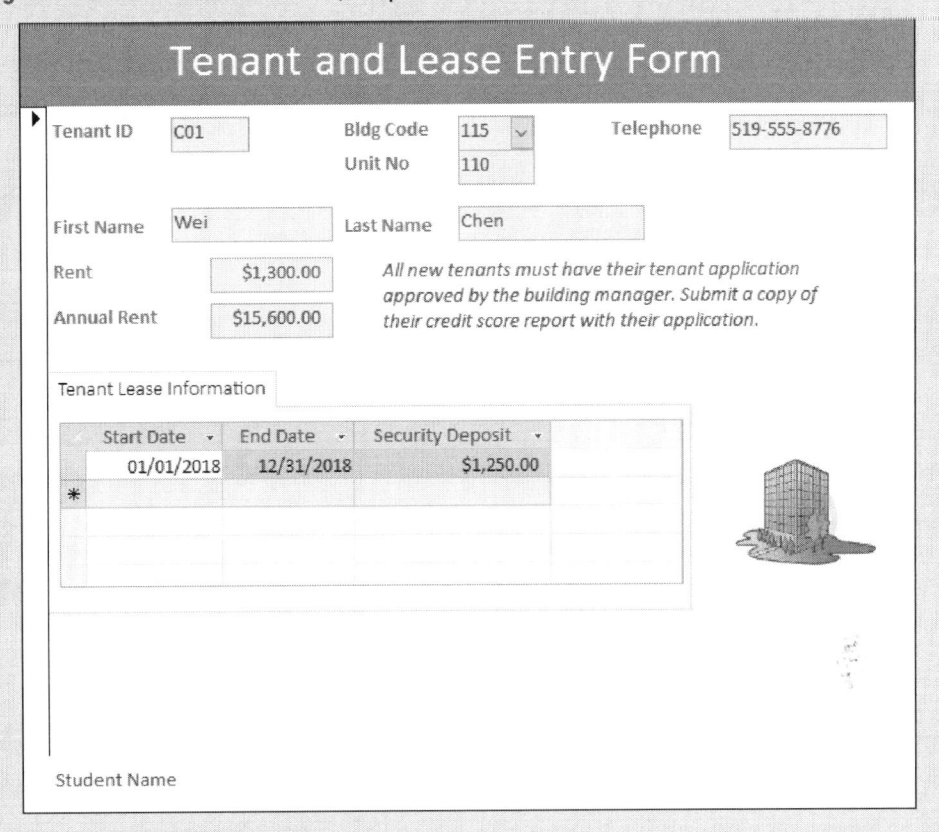

![Tenant and Lease Entry Form screenshot showing Tenant ID C01, Bldg Code 115, Unit No 110, Telephone 519-555-8776, First Name Wei, Last Name Chen, Rent $1,300.00, Annual Rent $15,600.00, with a note "All new tenants must have their tenant application approved by the building manager. Submit a copy of their credit score report with their application." and Tenant Lease Information showing Start Date 01/01/2018, End Date 12/31/2018, Security Deposit $1,250.00]

Writing Activities

The following activities give you the opportunity to practice your writing skills while demonstrating an understanding of some of the important Access features you have mastered in this unit. Use correct grammar, appropriate word choices, and clear sentence constructions when required.

Activity 1

Design Tables for Parking Information in the Property Management Database

The office manager at Benchmark Property Management would like to add tables to **U1-BenchmarkPropMgt.accdb** to store information about assigned parking at each building. Design and create one table to store parking rates and another table to track rental information for each parking spot using the information provided below. Create two lookup fields in the assigned parking table: one to look up the correct parking rate in the Rates table and another to look up the tenant's ID in the Tenants table. Add at least three records to test the tables.

Use the following information to assist with the table design:

Parking Rates
- Coventry Park charges $40 per month for parking.
- Mornington Place charges $61 per month for parking.
- Bayview Towers charges $80 per month for parking.

Assigned Parking Table
- Include fields to store the vehicle make, model, color, and license plate number of the tenant's vehicle that will be parked in the spot.
- Include a field to store the date the tenant began renting the spot.

In Microsoft Word, document your table design by including each table name and the fields created in each table, including the data type and field properties that you set (such as field size, caption, input mask, and so on). Indicate the primary key field in each table by typing an asterisk preceding the field name. Save the Word document and name it **U1-BenchmarkPropMgt**. Print the document and then exit Word.

Activity 2

Design Tables for a Soccer League Database

You are assisting the volunteer registration coordinator for a local soccer league. The registration coordinator would like to create an Access database to store information about this season's soccer players. He wants to be able to extract reports by age category to develop team lists and generate financial reports for the league treasurer. Design and create tables in a new database named **U1-SoccerRegn.accdb**. The registration coordinator has given you a sample registration form to help you design the tables. Refer to the sample form shown in Figure WB-U1.3.

Create one data entry form to enter information into the tables and add at least five records to test the table and form design. Print all the records using the form. Design and create a prompted query that will print a list of soccer players selecting records by age category. Design and create another query to print the names of the soccer players registered for the current season, including the registration fee paid. Add a *Total* row in the query results datasheet to show the total registration fees collected. Run each query to test the query design and print the query results datasheets.

In Microsoft Word, create a one-page quick reference guide for the registration coordinator and treasurer that provides instructions on how to open the database and use the data entry form, prompted query, and registration fee query. Include in the instructions how to print objects in the database, including how to print a selected form. Save the Word document and name it **U1-SoccerRegistration**. Print the document and then exit Word.

Figure WB-U1.3 Writing Activity 2

Minor League Soccer Registration

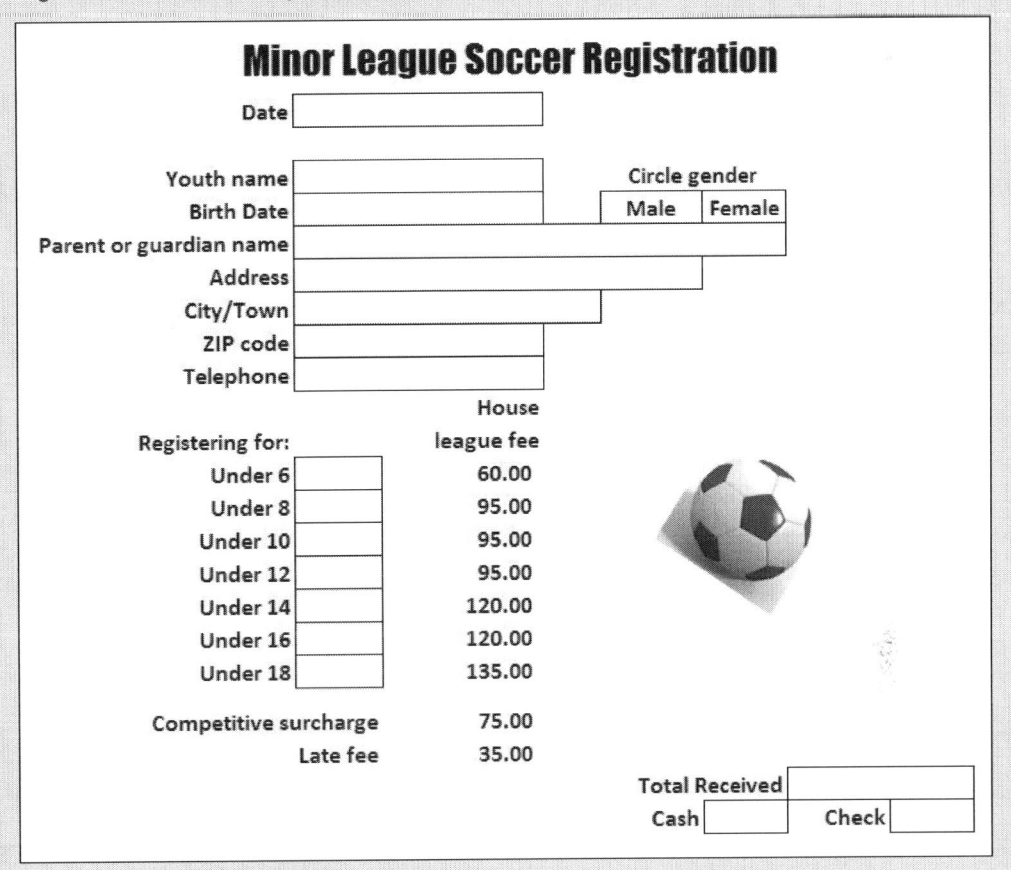

Date

Youth name
Birth Date
Parent or guardian name
Address
City/Town
ZIP code
Telephone

Circle gender
Male   Female

Registering for: House league fee
Under 6   60.00
Under 8   95.00
Under 10   95.00
Under 12   95.00
Under 14   120.00
Under 16   120.00
Under 18   135.00

Competitive surcharge   75.00
Late fee   35.00

Total Received
Cash   Check

Internet Research

Plan Your Volunteer Work

You want to volunteer each week but are not sure what organization is a good fit with your skills and interests. As you begin to consider where to donate your time and expertise, you decide to use your newly learned Access skills to develop a volunteer organization database that you can share with your friends and relatives.

To create your database, research five to eight organizations in your area that need volunteers on a regular basis. Pick a variety of organizations so that most people will find at least one organization in the database that appeals to them. Design tables in Access in a new database named **U1-VolunteerOrg.accdb** to store each organization's name, address, telephone number, and volunteer coordinator (if applicable). Include a field with notes about the organization's mission. Look for annual fund-raising events that need volunteers and include an Events table related to the organization. Design and create a form for data entry and use the form to input records for the organizations that you researched. Print all the records using the form.

Using Microsoft Word, create a brief document with instructions for your friends and relatives on how to open the database, browse records using the form, and print information. Save the document, naming it **U1-VolunteerInfo**, and then print it.

Microsoft Access Level 2

Unit 2

Advanced Reports, Access Tools, and Customizing Access

Chapter 5 Creating and Using Custom Reports

Chapter 6 Using Access Tools and Managing Objects

Chapter 7 Automating, Customizing, and Securing Access

Chapter 8 Integrating Access Data

Unit 2 Performance Assessment

Microsoft® Access®
Creating and Using Custom Reports

CHAPTER 5

Study Tools
Study tools include a presentation and a list of chapter Quick Steps and Hint margin notes. Use these resources to help you further develop and review skills learned in this chapter.

Concepts Check
SNAP Check your understanding by identifying application tools used in this chapter. If you are a SNAP user, launch the Concepts Check from your Assignments page.

Recheck
SNAP Check your understanding by taking this quiz. If you are a SNAP user, launch the Recheck from your Assignments page.

Skills Exercise
SNAP Additional activities are available to SNAP users. If you are a SNAP user, access these activities from your Assignments page.

Skills Assessment

Assessment 1

Data Files

Create a Custom Report Using Design View
1. Open **5-ViewRite.accdb** and enable the content.
2. Create a new report using the Report Design button and build the report using the following specifications:
    a. Add a title in the *Report Header* section with the text TV Series and Sales.
    b. Add your name in a label control object at the left margin in the *Report Footer* section.
    c. Connect the TVSeries table to the report. Add the *ProdID*, *Title*, *SeasonNo*, *YearAired*, and *Price* fields from the table to the report.
    d. Move the label control objects for each field from the *Detail* section to the *Page Header* section, arranging the control objects horizontally in the order the fields appeared in the table. Place the objects as follows:

Field Label	Position of left edge of label control object on the horizontal ruler
Product ID	left margin
Title	1-inch mark
Season No	2.75-inch mark
Year Aired	3.5-inch mark
Price	4.5-inch mark

    e. Resize the *Page Header* section when finished so the extra space is removed.

f. Align each text box control object in the *Detail* section below the control object's associated label control object in the *Page Header* section as follows:

Text Box Control Object	Position of left edge of text box control object on the horizontal ruler
ProdID	left margin
Title	1-inch mark
SeasonNo	2.75-inch mark
YearAired	3.5-inch mark
Price	4.5-inch mark

g. Use Report view to check the alignment and width of control objects to make sure that data is not truncated in any of the control objects. Make adjustments as needed in Design view or Layout view.

h. Apply the Retrospect theme. Apply bold formatting to the title.

i. Insert a subreport into the *Detail* section using the following specifications. **Hint: You may first need to adjust the height of the** Detail *section to make room for the subreport if you have been using Layout view.*
 1) Use the CustWebOrders query and add the fields to the subreport in this order: *CustID, WebOrdID, DateOrd, ProdID,* and *Qty*.
 2) Accept the default link option to link the main report to the subreport by the *ProdID* field.
 3) Accept the default subreport name.
 4) Edit the text in the subreport label control object to *Web Sales*.
 5) View the report to ensure the data is properly linked.
 6) Remove the *ProdID* field (including the associated label control object) from the subreport, since this data is duplicated in the main report, and then move the *Qty* field (including the associated label control object) left to fill in the space.
 7) Move and/or resize the subreport control object as required.

j. Resize the *Detail* section so the section ends just below the subreport.

k. Change the font size to 12 points, apply bold formatting, and then change the border style to transparent for the *ProdID, Title, SeasonNo, YearAired,* and *Price* fields in the *Detail* section.

l. Improve the appearance of the report by making additional adjustments to the position, height, width, alignment, or formatting of the control objects. Do not add any elements, however, because you will continue to work on this report in the next assessment.

3. Save the report and name it *TVSeriesWithSales*.
4. Print and then close the report.

Assessment 2

Enhance the Report

1. With **5-ViewRite.accdb** open, display the TVSeriesWithSales report in Design view.
2. Add a page number in the center of each page using the *Page N of M* option.
3. Add the current date to the bottom right of each page, aligning the right edge of the control object in the *Page Footer* section at the 7-inch mark on the horizontal ruler. Use the third option.
4. Insert an appropriate online picture to the top right corner of the *Report Header*, resizing the control object to a suitable height and width and aligning the right edge of the control object at the 7-inch mark on the horizontal ruler. The image (**TVStudentFiles.png**) may also be accessed from the student data files. Adjust the position of the report title to center it horizontally within the title control object and position the title control object so it is horizontally centered in the *Report Header* section.

5. Draw a horizontal line under the report title control object. Change the line thickness to 2 points and apply the Tan, Accent 5, Darker 50% line color (second-to-last column, last row in the *Theme Colors* section).
6. Change all four margins for the report to 0.5 inch.
7. The diagonal green triangle appears on the Report Selector button after the margins are changed. Click the Error Checking button and then click *Select the Control Farthest to the Right*. This will remove the drop-down list and select the control object at the right edge of the report that would prevent resizing the grid to remove extra space. The control object selected is part of the date and time control objects that were added within the title control object in Step 3. Delete the control object. Click the Error Checking button again and then click *Remove Extra Report Space* at the drop-down list. Skip this step if a diagonal green triangle does not appear.
8. Save the report.
9. Print only the first page of the revised report and then close it.

Assessment 3 Create a New Report with Grouping and Totals

1. With **5-ViewRite.accdb** open, create a new report using the Report Wizard as follows:
   a. Use the CustWebOrders query and add all the fields to the report except *ProdID*.
   b. Group by the *DateOrd* field by month.
   c. Click the Next button to leave the sort field blank.
   d. Apply the *Stepped Layout* and *Landscape Orientation* options.
   e. Edit the report title to *WebSalesByDate*.
2. Preview both pages of the report and then switch to Design view.
3. Add your name in a label control object at the left edge of the *Report Footer* section.
4. Open the Group, Sort, and Total pane and make the following changes:
   a. Add a Sum function to the *Total Sale* column for each month. Show a grand total at the end of the report and a subtotal in the group footer. Apply the Currency format to the grand total and subtotal.
   b. Add a sort by the *LastName* field.
5. Add an appropriate label next to the Sum function in the *DateOrd Footer* section and next to the Sum function in the *Report Footer* section.
6. Edit the report title control object to *Web Sales by Date* and edit the *DateOrd by Month* label control object to *Month*.
7. Display the report in Print Preview and note any column widths that need to be adjusted or label control objects that need to be edited to display the entire entries. Switch to Design view or Layout view and adjust the column widths as necessary so that all the data is visible. Change *Quantity* to *Qty*.
8. Change the top and bottom margins to 0.75 inch, the left and right margins to 0.25 inch, and then print the report.
9. Save and then close the report.

Assessment 4 Create and Format a New Report with a Chart

1. With **5-ViewRite.accdb** open, create a new report using the Report Wizard as follows:
   a. Use the Customers table and add each customer's ID, name, and telephone fields to the report.
   b. Do not group or sort the report.
   c. Apply the *Columnar Layout* and *Landscape Orientation* options.
   d. Edit the report title to *CustomersWithChart*.
2. Preview the report.

3. Switch to Design view.
4. Insert a chart at the right side of the page next to each customer record using the following information:
   a. Use the CustWebOrders query.
   b. Add the *DateOrd* field and *TotalSale* field to the chart field list.
   c. Select a bar chart style. You determine which style to use.
   d. Accept the default chart layout that Access creates with *DateOrd by month* as the category axis label and *SumOfTotalSale* as the value axis.
   e. Accept *CustID* as the linked field for the report and chart.
   f. Edit the title for the chart to *Web Sales*.
5. Preview the report with the bar chart and then switch to Design view.
6. Edit the chart as follows:
   a. Change the chart type to a clustered column with a 3-D visual effect.
   b. Delete the legend.
   c. Change the color of the columns to dark purple (fifth column from the left, second row from the bottom).
7. Edit the report title to *Customers with Web Sales Chart*.
8. Add your name in a label control object at the bottom left of the report.
9. Make any other formatting changes that will improve the appearance of the report.
10. Print only the first page of the report.
11. Save and then close the report.

Assessment 5

Create a Custom Report Using the Blank Report Tool

1. With **5-ViewRite.accdb** open, create a new report using the Blank Report tool.
2. Add the first field named *CustID* from the Customers table and then apply the Stacked layout to the report.
3. Add the remaining fields from the Customers table below the *Customer ID* field. Make sure you release the mouse when the pink bar displays below *101* for the first *Customer ID*.
4. Widen the label control objects column so that *Street Address* does not wrap to a second line in the column.
5. Insert a tab control object right of the *Customer ID* field. Make sure you click the mouse when the pink bar displays right of *101*.
6. Remove the layout from the tab control object column and then lengthen the tab control object to align with the bottom of the *Email* field.
7. Expand the field list for the CustPymnt table and then add the following fields to the tab control object:

   CCType
   CCNumber
   CCExpMonth
   CCExpYear

8. Select all the label control objects in the tab control object and widen the objects so that all the label text is visible.
9. Save the report and name it *CustomersWithCreditCards*.
10. Delete the second page in the tab control object and then change the shape of the selected tab control object to Round Single Corner Rectangle.
11. Change the caption of the page in the tab control object to *Credit Card Details*.
12. Insert a title at the top of the report with the text *Customers with Payment Information*.
13. Print only the first page of the report.
14. Save and close the report and then close **5-ViewRite.accdb**.

Visual Benchmark

Data Files

Create Custom Reservations Report with Totals

1. Open **5-PawsParadise.accdb** and enable the content.
2. Review the partial report shown in Figure WB-5.1. It was created based on the Dog Owners table with the Dogs table added as a subreport. Create the report with the subreport with the following specifications and using your best judgment for formatting as well as alignment, spacing, sizing, and position of control objects:
    a. Apply the Ion Boardroom theme.
    b. Substitute another suitable online image if the one shown is not available. The image (**PawStudentFiles.png**) may also be accessed from the student data files.
    c. Add the current date and add page numbers to the bottom of each page.
    d. Edit the label control objects in the subreport as shown in Figure WB-5.1.
    e. Add your name in the *Report Footer* section.
3. Save the report, naming it *DogOwnersWithDogs*.
4. Preview the report. If necessary, return to Layout view or Design view to make adjustments. When finished, save and print the report.
5. Close the report and then close **5-PawsParadise.accdb**.

Figure WB-5.1 Partial View of Completed Visual Benchmark Report

Customer Number	First Name	Last Name	Home Telephone	Emergency Telephone
100	Shawn	Jenkins	(814) 555-8446	(814) 555-7469

Dog's Name	Breed	Color	Bordetella Vaccine?	Rabies Vaccine?	Play with other dogs?	Kennel Category
Abby	Labrador Retriever	Black	☑	☑	☑	V.I.P. Suite
Winnie	Cocker Spaniel	Buff	☑	☑	☑	V.I.P. Suite

Customer Number	First Name	Last Name	Home Telephone	Emergency Telephone
110	Valerie	McTague	(814) 555-3456	(814) 555-1495

Dog's Name	Breed	Color	Bordetella Vaccine?	Rabies Vaccine?	Play with other dogs?	Kennel Category
Chloe	Poodle	White	☑	☑	☐	Deluxe Suite

Customer Number	First Name	Last Name	Home Telephone	Emergency Telephone
115	Glen	Waters	(814) 555-7496	(814) 555-6124

Dog's Name	Breed	Color	Bordetella Vaccine?	Rabies Vaccine?	Play with other dogs?	Kennel Category
Barney	Pug	Black	☐	☐	☐	Indoor/Outdoor Suite

Customer Number	First Name	Last Name	Home Telephone	Emergency Telephone
120	Sofia	Ramos	(814) 555-6523	(814) 555-8769

Dog's Name	Breed	Color	Bordetella Vaccine?	Rabies Vaccine?	Play with other dogs?	Kennel Category
Apollo	Greyhound	Cream	☑	☑	☑	Indoor/Outdoor Suite
Murphy	Bichon Frise	White	☑	☑	☐	Indoor/Outdoor Suite

Case Study

Part 1

Data Files

Continuing your work as an intern at Hillsdale Realty, your next task is to create reports for management. Open **5-HillsdaleRealty.accdb** and enable the content. For each report created, add your name in a label control object in the *Report Footer* section. The first report has been requested by the office manager. She uses the SalesByAgentWithComm query frequently but has asked for a report that provides the information in a more useful format. Specifically, the office manager would like the report to be organized with each individual agent's sales together, showing the total value of sales and commissions earned for each agent and sorted by the dates the listings sold. The office manager would also like to see grand totals and the percentage of the grand total that each agent achieved for the sale prices and commissions earned. Design and create the report, including features such as page numbers, date and time, and graphics. The image (**SaleStudentFile.png**) may also be accessed from the student data files. Save the report and name it appropriately. Print the report with the top and bottom margins set to 0.5 inch, the left and right margins set to 0.25 inch, and then make sure that an entire group is kept together on the same page.

Part 2

The office manager at Hillsdale Realty would like to have a printout of the listings with the clients' preferences and the agents attached to the listings grouped by city. (Note that not all the listings have preferences recorded but the office manager wants to see all the listings in the report.) You determine an appropriate sort order within each city's group of records. Design and create the report. Save the report and name it appropriately. Print the report with a top margin of 0.75 inch; the bottom, left, and right margins set to 0.25 inch; and then make sure that an entire group is kept together on the same page. *Hint: Consider first creating a query with the relevant fields needed from the Listings, Preferences, and Agents tables and then base the report on the query. For one of the relationships in the query, you will need to modify the join properties.*

Part 3

The accountant at Hillsdale Realty would like to have a report that shows the number of days a listing that has sold was on the market, as well as the average number of days it took to sell a listing by city. Design and create the report. Save the report and name it appropriately. Print the report with the top and bottom margins set to 0.75 inch and the left and right margins set to 0.25 inch. *Hint: Create a query using the Listings and SalesAndComm tables that includes a calculated field for the number of days a listing was on the market and then base the report on the query.*

Part 4

In Access Help, research how to create a summary report (a report without the record details shown within a group). The accountant at Hillsdale Realty would like to have a compacted version of the report you created for the office manager in Part 1 that shows the totals only for individual agents. Open that report and use *Save Object As* to create a copy of it. You determine an appropriate new name. In the new copy of the report, modify the design to create the report for the accountant. Print the new report, changing the page setup options as needed to fit the entire report on one page. Save and then close the report. Close **5-HillsdaleRealty.accdb**.

Microsoft® Access®
Using Access Tools and Managing Objects

CHAPTER 6

Study Tools

Study tools include a presentation and a list of chapter Quick Steps and Hint margin notes. Use these resources to help you further develop and review skills learned in this chapter.

Concepts Check

SNAP Check your understanding by identifying application tools used in this chapter. If you are a SNAP user, launch the Concepts Check from your Assignments page.

Recheck

SNAP Check your understanding by taking this quiz. If you are a SNAP user, launch the Recheck from your Assignments page.

Skills Exercise

SNAP Additional activities are available to SNAP users. If you are a SNAP user, access these activities from your Assignments page.

Skills Assessment

Assessment 1

Create a New Database Using a Template

1. Create a new database named **6-Assets.accdb** using the Desktop Asset Tracking template. Enable the content. Close the Getting Started with Assets form.
2. Spend a few moments opening and viewing various objects within the database. Close all the objects when finished with them, including the Asset List form.
3. Open the Contact Details form, add the following record using the form, and then close the form. Substitute your names in the *First Name* and *Last Name* fields. Leave all fields not mentioned blank.

First Name	(Enter student's first name)
Last Name	(Enter student's last name)
Company	River Assets
Business Phone	212-555-5559

4. Open the Asset Details form, add the following records using the form, and then close the form.

Item	Web Server
Category	(1) Category
Manufacturer	Edge Industries
Model	TrueEdge 6500
Acquired Date	(Enter the current date.)
Purchase Price	1850.00
Current Value	1850.00
Condition	(Click *(1) Great* at the drop-down list.)
Location	(Click *(1) Location* at the drop-down list.)

Owner	(Click your name at the drop-down list.)
Retired Date	(leave blank)
Description	(leave blank)
Attachments	(attach **WebServer.jpg**)

Item	Workstation
Category	(1) Category
Manufacturer	Edge Industries
Model	EdgeConnect 100
Acquired Date	(Enter the current date)
Purchase Price	985.00
Current Value	985.00
Condition	(Click *(1) Great* at the drop-down list.)
Location	(Click *(1) Location* at the drop-down list.)
Owner	(Click your name at the drop-down list.)
Retired Date	(leave blank)
Description	(leave blank)
Attachments	(attach **Workstation.jpg**)

5. Print the second record as displayed in the Asset Details form.
6. Close the form and then close **6-Assets.accdb**.

Assessment 2 — Create a Table Using an Application Parts Template

Data Files

1. Open **6-ViewRite.accdb** and enable the content.
2. Create a new group of objects related to tasks using the *Tasks* Quick Start option. When the Create Relationship Wizard begins, specify no relationship.
3. Using the TaskDetails form, add a record using the following information. Substitute your name for *Student Name* in the *Description* field.

Task	Set up backup Web server
Status	Not Started
Priority	(1) High
Start Date	Enter the current date
Due Date	Enter a due date that is one week from the current date
Attachments	(leave blank)
% Complete	(leave at default value of 0%)
Description	Configure hot server to be on standby in event of failover. Assigned to Student Name.

4. Close the form.
5. Open the Tasks table to view the record added to it using the form in Step 3. Close the table.
6. Print the selected record using the TaskDetails form.
7. Close the form.

Assessment 3 — Use Access Tools to Improve Design and Performance

1. With **6-ViewRite.accdb** open, use the Table Analyzer Wizard to analyze the CustPymnt table using the following information:
   a. Rename the new table that includes all the fields except the *CCType* field as *CustCreditCards*.
   b. Rename the new table that includes the *CCType* field as *CreditCardTypes*.
   c. Choose an appropriate field for the primary key field in the CustCreditCards table.

  d. If the wizard determines that the *Discover* card is a typographical error, choose *(Leave as is)* at the *Correction* drop-down list and then click the Next button.
  e. Create the query.
2. Close the Help window.
3. Delete the *CCType* field in the CustPymnt query. Adjust all the column widths to best fit and then print the query results datasheet with the left and right margins set to 0.25 inch.
4. Close the query, saving the layout changes.
5. Delete the CustPymnt_OLD table and any relationships involving it.
6. Split the database to create a front-end database and back-end database. Accept the default file name for the back-end database.
7. Close **6-ViewRite.accdb**.
8. Open **6-ViewRite_be.accdb** and enable the content.
9. Generate and print a report that provides the table and field property definitions for the CreditCardTypes table. Include the relationships in the report.
10. Close **6-ViewRite_be.accdb**.

Visual Benchmark

Activity 1

Create a Table to Store Groomers' Information

1. Open **6-PawsParadise.accdb** and enable the content.
2. Review the table shown in Figure WB-6.1 and create the new table in the database by copying the structure of the DogOwners table.
3. Modify the table design as needed and add the records shown in the figure. If necessary rename the table as shown.
4. Adjust all of the column widths and print the table on one page.
5. Close the table.

Figure WB-6.1 Visual Benchmark 1

Groomer ID	First Name	Last Name	Street Address	City	State	ZIP Code	Home Telephone	Hourly Rate
01	Max	Lahey	715 Irish Hollow	Smethport	PA	16749-	(814) 555-6253	$28.50
02	Juan	Modesta	117 Spring Drive	Bradford	PA	16701-	(814) 555-3845	$28.50
03	Pat	O'Connor	147 Lamont Drive	Bradford	PA	16701-	(814) 555-2118	$31.50
04	Greg	Walczak	22 Foster Square	Allegheny	PA	15212-	(814) 555-7448	$35.50
05	Melissa	Cochrane	140 Congress Street	Bradford	PA	16701-	(814) 555-6489	$28.50
				Bradford	PA			

Activity 2

Create a Form Template

1. With **6-PawsParadise.accdb** open, examine the control objects in the form named *Normal*, shown in Figure WB-6.2. Create a Normal form to be used as a template with the three control objects shown. Apply the Lavender, Accent 5, Darker 50% font color, bold font formatting, and the Lavender, Accent 5, Lighter 80% background color.
2. Create a new form for the Groomers table using the Form button in the Forms group on the Create tab. Decrease the width of the form title and text box control objects in the form so that one form will fit on one page. Print only the first form.
3. Save the Groomers form, accepting the default name *Groomers*.
4. Close the form and then close **6-PawsParadise.accdb**.

Figure WB-6.2 Visual Benchmark 2

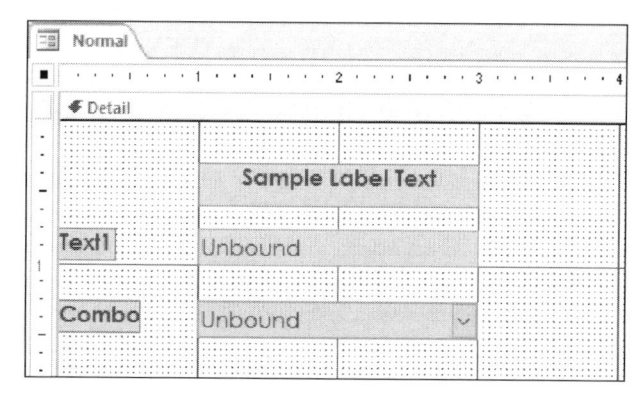

Case Study

Part 1

As an intern at Hillsdale Realty, you have been building a listings, sales, and commissions database over the past weeks. You decide to create a new database to store information about home shows and conferences that Hillsdale Realty attends as an exhibitor. To save time developing new objects, download the Desktop Event Management template to create a new database in the AL2C6 folder on your storage medium named **6-HillsdaleShows.accdb**. Enable the content, open the Events table in Design view, change the *Start Time* field and *End Time* field to be *Start Date* and *End Date* (respectively), and then add the following two trade show events to the database using the Event List form:

- The three-day Homebuilders Association Trade Show begins April 6, 2018, at the Phoenix Convention Center.
- The four-day Green Home Design Conference begins October 25, 2018, at the University of Phoenix Hohokam Campus.

The office manager likes the idea of tracking the trade shows in the database and has asked you to create a similar table to keep track of conferences that agents attend as visitors. Close the Event List form and display the Navigation pane. Copy the structure of the Events table to create a new table named *AgentConferences*. Modify the AgentConferences table to delete the *Attachments* field and add a new field to store the number of people the company will send to the show. Create a form for the AgentConferences table using the Form button and add the following record:

- Five employees will attend the three-day Window and Door Manufacturers Association Annual Conference that begins November 9, 2018, at the Georgia International Convention Center.

Preview the AgentConferences form in Print Preview. If necessary, make adjustments to fit the form on one page. Print the AgentConferences form with the first record displayed. Save and then close the form. Open the Event Details report. Print and then close the report. Close **6-HillsdaleShows.accdb**.

Part 2

Data Files

You want to see how Access tools can help you improve the design of the database you have been building for Hillsdale Realty over the past few months. Open **6-HillsdaleRealty.accdb** and enable the content. Use the Table Analyzer Wizard to analyze the Listings table. Accept the proposed table split, create appropriate table names, assign primary key fields, and create the query. Modify the query as needed to remove duplicate columns. Sort the query in ascending order by the *ListDate* field. Print the query results datasheet with all the column widths adjusted to best fit. Delete the original table with *_OLD* in the name, along with any relationships associated with that field.

Errors can occur when changes are made to a table after other objects have been created that are dependent on the table. Open the ListingsAndSales form. Notice the error in the control object named *City*. Since the Table Analyzer Wizard split the original Listings table on the *City* field, the original field added to the form no longer exists. Display the form in Design view. Open the Property Sheet task pane and change the *Record Source* property to *ListingsNew* and then close the Property Sheet task pane. Delete the *City* control object. Add a Combo Box control object to hold the city data. Make changes to the new field to be consistent with the other control objects in the form.

Part 3

Use the Performance Analyzer to analyze the entire Hillsdale Realty database. When the Listings table was split in Part 2, the relationships between the original Listings table and other objects were removed, leaving the new split table unrelated to any other table. Select and optimize entries in the *Analysis Results* list box that will create the relationships between the new Listings table and other objects.

Notice that for all the fields that store identification numbers—such as *AgentID*, *ClientID*, *ListingNo*, and *QuotaID*—the idea has been proposed that the data type should be changed from Short Text to Long Integer. Long Integer is not actually a data type but a field size setting for a numeric field. Research data types in Access Help. Specifically, find out the difference between assigning a field the Short Text data type and Number data type. Using Microsoft Word, compose a memo to your instructor that includes the following information:

- An explanation of the use of the Short Text data type
- An explanation of the use of the Number data type
- Your recommendation of which data type should be used for the four *ID* fields in the database and why

Save the memo and name it **6-HillsdaleDBAnalysisMemo**. Print the memo and then exit Word. In the database, open the Relationships window. Delete the original Listings table from the window and display the new Listings table name to show the relationships created when the database was optimized. Rearrange the table field list boxes so the join lines are easy to follow, establish referential integrity and cascading options, and then generate a relationships report. Print the relationships report. Save and close the relationships report and then close **6-HillsdaleRealty.accdb**.

Microsoft® Access®
Automating, Customizing, and Securing Access

CHAPTER 7

Study Tools
Study tools include a presentation and a list of chapter Quick Steps and Hint margin notes. Use these resources to help you further develop and review skills learned in this chapter.

Concepts Check
Check your understanding by identifying application tools used in this chapter. If you are a SNAP user, launch the Concepts Check from your Assignments page.

Recheck
Check your understanding by taking this quiz. If you are a SNAP user, launch the Recheck from your Assignments page.

Skills Exercise
Additional activities are available to SNAP users. If you are a SNAP user, access these activities from your Assignments page.

Skills Assessment

Assessment 1

Data Files

Create and Run Macros
1. Open **7-ViewRite.accdb** and enable the content.
2. Create the following macros. Run each macro to make sure it works properly and then close it.
   a. Create a macro named *RPTMedia* that opens the ProductsOrderedByMedia report; use the macro action *OpenReport*. In the Macro task pane, change *Report* to *Print Preview* in the View Option argument option box.
   b. Create a macro named *RPTWebSales* to open the WebSalesByDate report in Report view.
   c. Create a macro named *FORMCustOrd* that opens the WebCustOrders form in Form view, activates the control object named *LastName*, and then opens the Find and Replace dialog box. Test the macro using the customer last name *Gallagher*.
3. Open the RPTMedia macro in Design view. Click the File tab, click the *Print* option, and then click *Print* at the Print backstage area. At the Print Macro Definition dialog box, remove check marks as necessary until only the *Actions and Arguments* check box is checked and then click OK. Close the Macro Builder window.
4. Print the FORMCustOrd macro and RPTWebSales macro by completing steps similar to Step 3.

Assessment 2 — **Edit a Macro and Assign Macros to Command Buttons**

1. With **7-ViewRite.accdb** open, edit the FORMCustOrd macro to remove the *OpenForm* action. Save and close the revised macro. Rename the FORMCustOrd macro in the Navigation pane as *FINDLastName*.
2. Create command buttons to run macros as follows:
   a. Open the WebCustOrders form in Design view and then create a command button at the right side of the title in the *Form Header* section that runs the FINDLastName macro. Adjust the size of the title, if necessary. You determine the appropriate text to display on the button and a name for the command button. Format the button using the Light 1 Outline, Colored Fill - Green, Accent 6 quick style. Save and close the form.
   b. Open the TVSeries form in Design view and create two command buttons as follows:
      - A button at the left side of the form at the bottom of the *Detail* section that runs the RPTMedia macro
      - A button at the right side of the form at the bottom of the *Detail* section, parallel to the new macro button on the left side, that runs the RPTWebSales macro

      You determine the appropriate text to display on each button and a name for each button. Format each button with the quick style used in Step 2a. Save and then close the form.
3. Open each form, test the button(s) to make sure the correct form or report displays, and then close each form or report.
4. Open the WebCustOrders form in Form view. Insert a screen shot of the database window showing the custom button in a new Microsoft Word document using either the Screenshot button in the Illustrations group on the Insert tab or the Print Screen key and the Paste feature. Switch back to Access and open the TVSeries form in Form view. Insert a screenshot of the database window below the first image in the Microsoft Word document. Type your name a few lines below the screen images and add any other identifying information as instructed. Save the Microsoft Word document with the name **7-FormWindows**. Print **7-FormWindows.docx** and then exit Word.
5. Close both forms.

Assessment 3 — **Create a Navigation Form and Configure Database Options**

1. With **7-ViewRite.accdb** open, create a Navigation form using the following information:
   a. Apply the Vertical Tabs, Left style.
   b. Add the WebCustOrders form as the first tab.
   c. Add the TVSeries form as the second tab.
   d. Add the ProductsOrderedByMedia report as the third tab.
   e. Add the WebSalesByDate report as the fourth tab.
   f. Save the form, naming it *MainMenu*.
2. In Layout view or Design view, edit the MainMenu Navigation form as follows:
   a. Delete the logo container object.
   b. Edit the text in the *Title* control object to read *ViewRite* and resize the object so the right edge of the control ends just after the title text. In other words, adjust the width of the control object so it is only as wide as needed to display the title text.
   c. Apply the Light 1 Outline, Colored Fill - Green, Accent 6 quick style to all of the tabs, including the [Add New] tab.

d. Change the Caption property for the first tab to *Customer Orders*.
e. Change the Caption property for the second tab to *TV Series*.
f. Change the Caption property for the third tab to *Orders by Media*.
g. Change the Caption property for the fourth tab to *Sales by Month*.
3. Create a new macro named *ExitDB* that will save all objects when exiting Access. Assign the macro to a command button in the *Form Header* section of the MainMenu form. You determine the appropriate text to display on the button and a name for the button. Format it with the same Quick Style used for the tabs. Save and close the MainMenu form.
4. Set the MainMenu form as the startup display form.
5. Create an application title for the database with the text *ViewRite Orders Database*.
6. Hide the Navigation pane.
7. Turn on the *Check for new unassociated labels* error-checking option. **Note: Skip this step if you did not complete Project 3c, in which this option was turned off**.
8. Close and then reopen the database to test the startup options. Click each tab in the MainMenu form to make sure the correct form or report displays.
9. With the database open at the MainMenu form and the Customer Orders tab selected, insert a screenshot of the database window in a new Microsoft Word document using either the Screenshot button in the Illustrations group on the Insert tab or the Print Screen key and the Paste feature. Type your name a few lines below the screenshot and add any other identifying information as instructed. Save the Microsoft Word document with the name **7-MainMenu**. Print **7-MainMenu.docx** and then exit Word.

Assessment 4

Customize the Ribbon

1. With **7-ViewRite.accdb** open, export your customizations to your storage medium. Save the file as **7-ViewRiteCustomizations.exportedUI**.
2. Add a new tab between the Home tab and Create tab. Rename the tab using your first and last names. Add a new group to the new tab so there are two new groups. Rename the first group *Formatting* and the second group *Maintenance*.
3. Select *All Commands* in the *Choose commands from* option box and then add the Font Color, Format Cells, Format Painter, and Line Color buttons to the Formatting group.
4. Select *File Tab* in the *Choose commands from* option box and then add the Access 2002-2003 Database, Back Up Database, and Compact & Repair Database buttons to the Maintenance group.
5. With the database open at the MainMenu form, insert a screenshot of the database window showing the new custom tab in a new Microsoft Word document using either the Screenshot button in the Illustrations group on the Insert tab or the Print Screen key and the Paste feature. Type your name a few lines below the screenshot and add any other identifying information as instructed. Save the Microsoft Word document with the name **7-VRRibbon**. Print **7-VRRibbon.docx** and then exit Word.
6. Import the customization file saved in Step 1 to reset the ribbon back to your institution's settings.
7. Use the Exit button in the MainMenu form to exit the database and close Access.

Visual Benchmark

Data Files

Automate and Customize a Reservation Database

1. Open **7-PawsParadise.accdb** and enable the content.
2. Review the database window shown in Figure WB-7.1. Create the Navigation form as shown, including the command buttons and required macros assigned to the command buttons. Set the required startup and Navigation pane options.
3. Check with your instructor for instructions on whether to print the macros and a screen image of the database window.

Figure WB-7.1 Visual Benchmark

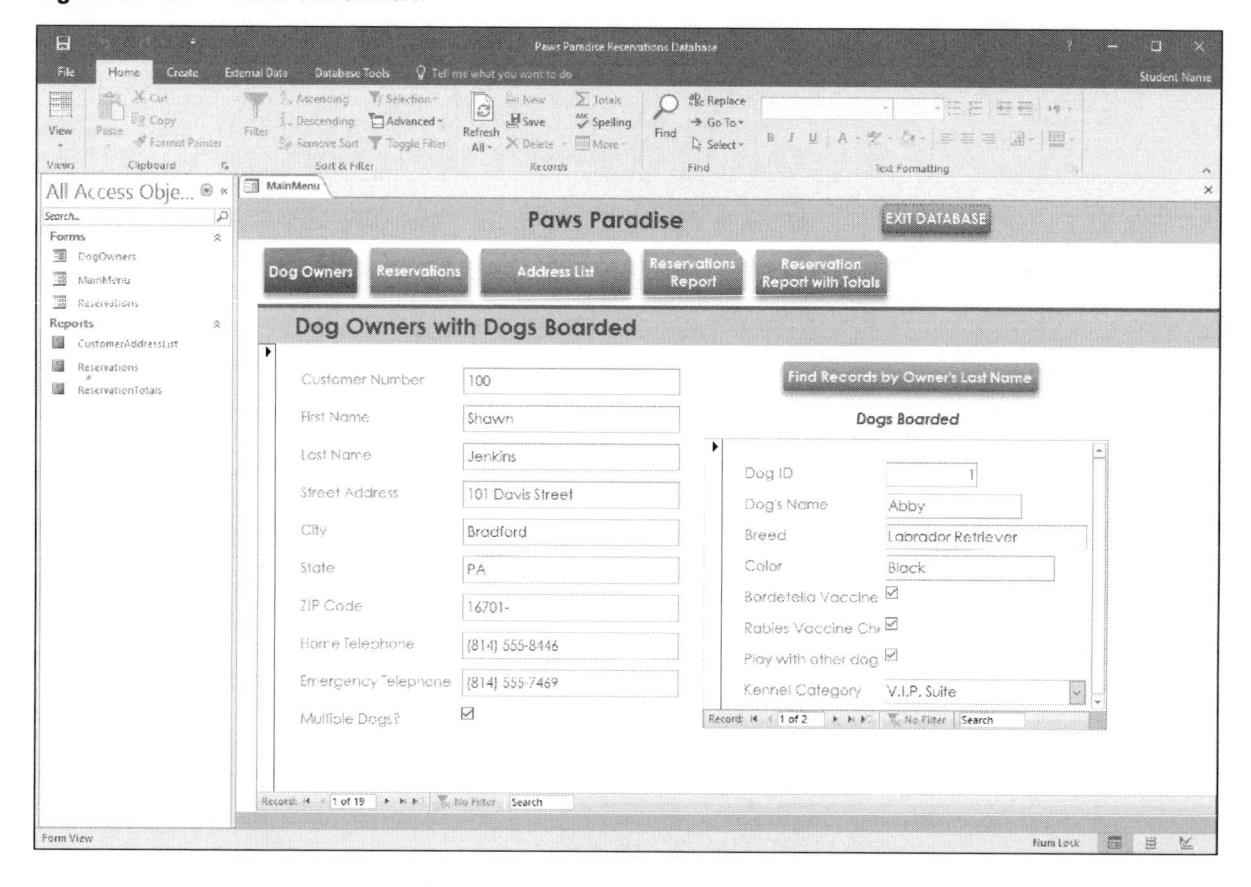

Case Study

Part 1

Data Files

As you near completion of your work as an intern at Hillsdale Realty, you decide to automate the database to make using the application easier for the next intern. Open **7-HillsdaleRealty.accdb** and enable the content. Create three macros to accomplish the tasks in the bulleted list below. You determine the appropriate macro names.

- Move to the *AgentLName* control and open the Find and Replace dialog box.
- Move to the *ListingNo* control and open the Find and Replace dialog box.
- Save all objects when exiting the database.

Assign the first macro as a command button in the Agents form. Assign the second macro as a command button in the ListingsAndSales form. In both forms, determine where to position the button, what text to display on the button, how to format the button, and what to name the button. The third macro will be assigned as a command button in the *Form Header* section of the MainMenu form in Part 2. Check with your instructor for instructions on whether to print the macros and a screen image of the Agents form and ListingsAndSales form, showing each command button.

Part 2

Create a navigation form to be used as a main menu for the Hillsdale Realty database; it should display the Agents form, ListingsAndSales form, and two reports. Set the navigation form to display automatically when the database is opened. Add an appropriate application title for the database and hide the tables, queries, and macros in the Navigation pane. Assign the macro to exit the database as a button in the main menu form. Edit the main menu form as necessary to show descriptive labels on the tabs; also apply other formatting enhancements. Close and reopen the database to test your startup options. Test each menu tab to make sure each option works. Check with your instructor for instructions on whether to print a screen image of the database window with the main menu form displayed.

Part 3

In Access Help, research other options for customizing Access in the *Current Database* section of the Access Options dialog box. Using Microsoft Word, compose a memo in your own words and addressed to your instructor that provides information on three options not discussed in this chapter. Save the memo in Word with the name **7-PackageMemo**. Print the memo and then exit Word.

Microsoft® Access®
Integrating Access Data

CHAPTER 8

Study Tools

Study tools include a presentation and a list of chapter Quick Steps and Hint margin notes. Use these resources to help you further develop and review skills learned in this chapter.

Concepts Check

Check your understanding by identifying application tools used in this chapter. If you are a SNAP user, launch the Concepts Check from your Assignments page.

Recheck

Check your understanding by taking this quiz. If you are a SNAP user, launch the Recheck from your Assignments page.

Skills Exercise

Additional activities are available to SNAP users. If you are a SNAP user, access these activities from your Assignments page.

Skills Assessment

Assessment 1

Data Files

Import and Link Objects from Another Access Database

1. Open **8-ViewRiteStock.accdb** and enable the content.
2. Using **8-ViewRite.accdb** as the data source file, integrate the following objects into the active database:
   a. Import the TVSeries form.
   b. Link to the TVSeries, WebOrders, and WebOrderDetails tables.
3. Display the Relationships window, add the TVSeries table, and then create a relationship between the TVSeries table and TVSeriesCosts table using the *ProdID* field. Save and close the Relationships window.
4. Modify the TVSeries form as follows:
   a. Open the form in Design view.
   b. Delete the label and text box control objects for the following fields: *Year Aired*, *Genre*, *DVD*, *Blu-ray*, *Download*, and *Multiformat*. This will leave the form with seven fields: *Product ID*, *Title*, *Season No*, *Episodes*, *Price*, *Current Discount*, and *Discount Price*.
   c. Remove the space left by deleting the fields by moving up the three label and text box control objects.
   d. Display the Field List task pane and make sure that all the tables are visible in the pane. Expand the field list for the TVSeriesCosts table.
   e. Add the *Cost* field below the *DiscountPrice* field in the form.
   f. Align, resize, and format the field as necessary so the cost price displays similarly to the selling price.
   g. Change the form title to *Inventory and Pricing*.

5. Save the revised form, print the first record, and then close the form.
6. Open the ProdCostsWithSupp query in Design view and modify it as follows:
   a. Add the TVSeries table to the query.
   b. Add the *Price* field to the query design grid, placing it between the *SeasonNo* and *Cost* columns.
   c. Right of the *Cost* column, add a calculated column named *GrossProfit* that subtracts the cost from the price. Change the caption to *Gross Profit*.
7. Save the revised query and then run the query.
8. Print the query in landscape orientation and then close the query.

Assessment 2

Data Files

Import a Text File

1. With **8-ViewRiteStock.accdb** open, make a backup copy and then append records from a text file using the following information:
   - Name the backup database file **8-ViewRiteStock_yyyy-mm-dd.accdb**, where *yyyy-mm-dd* represents today's date. Save this database in the DatabaseBackUps folder that you created in Project 1a.
   - The data source file is named **TVSeriesCost.csv**.
   - Append a copy of the records to the end of the existing TVSeriesCosts table.
   - Save the import steps using the default name and type the following description: Import of new TV Series titles from TVSeriesCost.csv.
2. Open the TVSeriesCosts table and print the table datasheet.
3. Close the datasheet.
4. Close **8-ViewRiteStock.accdb**.

Assessment 3

Data Files

Export and Publish Access Data

1. Open **8-ViewRite.accdb** and enable the content.
2. Export the CustWebOrders query to a comma delimited text file using the following information:
   - Include the field names and remove the quotation marks.
   - Use the default file name.
   - Save the export steps and type the following description: Export the customers' web orders to a text file.
3. Open Notepad and then open and print **CustWebOrders.txt**.
4. Exit Notepad.

Assessment 4

Secure the Database

1. With **8-ViewRite.accdb** open, save a copy of the database as an ACCDE file in the same folder and using the same file name.
2. Close **8-ViewRite.accdb**.
3. Open **8-ViewRite.accde**.
4. Insert a screenshot of the database window in a new Microsoft Word document using the Screenshot button in the Illustrations group on the Insert tab or the Print Screen key and the Paste feature. Type your name a few lines below the screenshot and add other identifying information as instructed. Save the Microsoft Word document and name it **8-ViewRiteACCDE**. Print **8-ViewRiteACCDE.docx** and then exit Word.
5. Close **8-ViewRite.accde**.

Visual Benchmark

Data Files

Analyze a Reservation Database

1. Open **8-PawsParadise.accdb** and enable the content.
2. Using **8-PawsGroomers.accdb** as the data source file, integrate the following objects into the active database:
   a. Import the Groomers form.
   b. Link to the Groomers table.
3. Modify the Groomers form as shown in Figure WB-8.1. The image, **Grooming.png**, may be accessed from the student data files.
4. Save a copy of the database as an ACCDE file.
5. Close **8-PawsParadise.accdb**.
6. Open **8-PawsParadise.accde**. Check with your instructor for instructions on whether to print a screen image of the database window, as shown below.
7. Close **8-PawsParadise.accde**.

Figure WB-8.1 Visual Benchmark

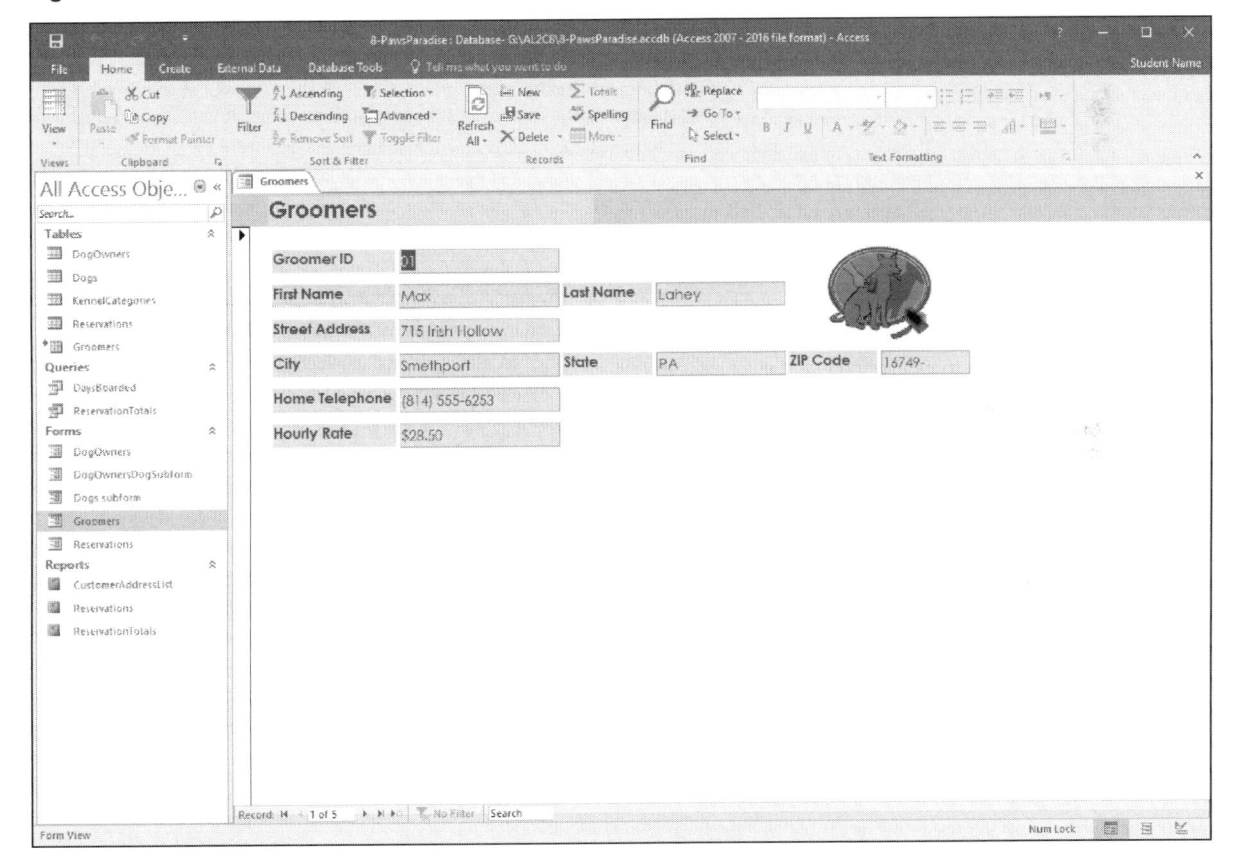

Case Study

Part 1

Data Files

As an intern at Hillsdale Realty, you have been asked by the office manager to export the Listings table data from the database for use in a custom software package that accepts comma separated data files. Open **8-HillsdaleRealty.accdb** and enable the content. Create a text file for the office manager, including field names and quotations marks as text qualifiers. Save the export steps because the office manager has told you that producing this data exchange file will be required often. Print the text file for your records.

Part 2

The office manager at Hillsdale Realty has asked you to assist her with backing up the HillsdaleRealty database. Create a backup copy of the database, name it **8-HillsdaleRealty_yyyy-mm-dd.accdb** (where *yyyy-mm-dd* is the current date), and then place it in the DatabaseBackUps folder that you created in Project 1a. Using **8-HillsdaleRealty.accdb**, create an ACCDE file called **8-HillsdaleRealty.accde**.

Part 3

Open a Help window and search using the phrase *discontinued features*. Click the Discontinued features and modified functionality in Access hyperlink. Read the information in Help and then use Microsoft Word to compose a memo in your own words addressed to your instructor that answers the following questions:

- Why can an Access 97 database not be opened in Access 2016?
- What must be done to an Access 97 database to be able to open it in Access 2016?
- What was the last version of Access to offer an option to create PivotCharts and PivotTables?

Save the memo in Word and name it **8-DiscontinuedMemo**. Print the memo and then exit Word.

Microsoft Access Level 2

Unit 2 Performance Assessment

Data Files

Before beginning unit work, copy the AL2U2 folder to your storage medium and then make AL2U2 the active folder.

Assessing Proficiency

In this unit, you have learned to design and create reports with grouping, sorting, totals, and subreports; to use Access tools to analyze tables and improve database efficiency; to automate a database using macros and a Navigation form; to configure startup options and customize the database and Navigation pane; and to integrate Access data with other programs. If you have problems accessing any online images, .png files for the Assessments can be obtained from the student data files.

Assessment 1

Import Data from Text Files and Create Reports for a Property Management Database

Data Files

1. Open **U2-BenchmarkPropMgt.accdb** and enable the content. In this unit, you will continue working with the residential property management database for Benchmark Property Management that you started in Unit 1. The database design and objects have since been modified based on feedback from the property manager and office staff.
2. Create a folder called *DatabaseBackUps*. Make a backup copy of the database and place it in the new folder. Name the backup database **U2-BenchmarkPropMgt_yyyy-mm-dd**, where *yyyy-mm-dd* represents today's date.
3. With **U2-BenchmarkPropMgt.accdb** open, import data into tables from two text files as follows. Save each set of import specifications for future use. Use the default name and determine an appropriate description for each set of import steps. Because referential integrity is being enforced on the relationship, the Tenants text file must be imported before the Leases text file.
   a. Append the data in the **TenantsU2.csv** text file to the Tenants table.
   b. Append the data in the **LeasesU2.csv** text file to the Leases table.
4. Design and create reports as follows:
   a. Design and create a report based on the LeasesByBldg query with all the fields included except the building code field. Group the records by

building name and sort them by unit number within each group. Name the report *BuildingsAndLeases*. Include the current date and page numbers in the page footer. Add your name as the report designer in the report footer and insert an appropriate online picture in the report header. Alternatively, an image (**buildings.png**) may be accessed from the student data files. You determine the remaining layout and formatting elements, including a descriptive report title.

b. Design and create a report based on the RentalIncome query with all the fields included except the building code field. Group the records by building name and sort them by unit number within each group. Name the report *IncomeByBuilding*. Sum the rent and annual rent columns and count the unit numbers. Show the statistics in the group footer and as grand totals at the end of the report. Include appropriate labels to describe the statistics and format the values to a suitable numeric format, if necessary. Add your name as the report designer in the report footer and insert an online picture in the report header. Alternatively, an image (**buildings.png**) may be accessed from the student data files. You determine the remaining layout and formatting elements, including a descriptive report title.

5. Print the BuildingAndLeases and IncomeByBuilding reports.

Assessment 2 — Use Access Tools to Improve the Property Management Database Design

1. With **U2-BenchmarkPropMgt.accdb** open, use the Performance Analyzer feature to analyze all the objects in the database. In the Analysis Results list, use the Optimize button to fix each suggestion item. (A suggestion item displays with a green question mark.)
2. Use the Database Splitter to split the database into two files to create a back-end database. Accept the default file name at the Create Back-end Database dialog box.
3. Close **U2-BenchmarkPropMgt.accdb**.
4. Open **U2-BenchmarkPropMgt_be.accdb** and enable the content.
5. Use the Database Documenter feature to generate a table definition report for the Leases table. Change the options as follows: Set *Include for Table* to *Properties* and *Relationships*; set *Include for Fields* to *Names, Data Types, and Sizes*; and set *Include for Indexes* to *Nothing*. Print and then close the report.
6. Close **U2-BenchmarkPropMgt_be.accdb**.

Assessment 3 — Automate the Property Management Database with Macros and Command Buttons

1. Open **U2-BenchmarkPropMgt.accdb** and enable the content if necessary.
2. Create the following macros. After creating each macro, run the macro to make sure it works properly, print each macro's definition, and then close the macro.
   a. Create a QLeasesByTenant macro that opens the LeasesByTenant query in Datasheet view and Edit mode. Use the macro action *OpenQuery*.
   b. Create a QLeaseTerms macro that opens the LeaseTermsAndDeposits query in Datasheet view and Edit mode. Use the macro action *OpenQuery*.
   c. Create a RBldLeases macro that opens the BuildingsAndLeases report in report view. Use the macro action *OpenReport*.
   d. Create a RIncome macro that opens the IncomeByBuilding report in report view. Use the macro action *OpenReport*.
3. Open the BldgsAndMgrs form in Design view.

4. Create two command buttons in the *Form Header* section: one that runs the RBldgLeases macro and another that runs the RIncome macro. You determine the placement of the buttons within the section, the text to display on the face of each button, and the name to assign each button.
5. Test each button to make sure the macro displays the correct report. Insert a screenshot of the BldgsAndMgrs form with the buttons displayed in a new Microsoft Word document. Create the screenshot using the Screenshot button in the Illustrations group on the Insert tab or the Print Screen key and the Paste feature. Type your name a few lines below the screenshot and add any other identifying information as instructed. Print the document and then exit Word without saving.
6. Make sure all the objects are closed.

Assessment 4

Create a Navigation Form and Configure Startup Options for the Property Management Database

1. With **U2-BenchmarkPropMgt.accdb** open, create a Navigation form named *MainMenu* using the Horizontal Tabs style with forms and reports in the following tab order:
   - BldgsAndMgrs form
   - TenantsAndLeases form
   - BuildingsAndLeases report
   - IncomeByBuilding report
2. Edit the form title and delete the logo container object. You determine the appropriate text to replace *Navigation Form*.
3. Edit the tab captions. You determine the appropriate text for each tab.
4. Create a macro named *ExitDB* that saves all objects when quitting Access and then create a command button at the right end of the MainMenu *Form Header* section that runs the macro. You determine the text to display on the face of the button and the name to assign the button.
5. Display the form in Form view and then click each tab to make sure the correct form or report displays.
6. Set the MainMenu form to display as the startup form, add an appropriate application title for the database, and then hide the Navigation pane.
7. Close and then reopen **U2-BenchmarkPropMgt.accdb**.
8. Insert a screenshot of the database in a new Microsoft Word document using the Screenshot button in the Illustrations group on the Insert tab or the Print Screen key and the Paste feature. Type your name a few lines below the screenshot and add any other identifying information as instructed. Print the Word document and then exit Word without saving.

Assessment 5

Configure Security for the Property Management Database

1. With **U2-BenchmarkPropMgt.accdb** open, make an ACCDE file from the database. Save the copy in the same folder and use the same file name.
2. Close **U2-BenchmarkPropMgt.accdb**.
3. Open **U2-BenchmarkPropMgt.accde**.
4. Change the database startup option to display the Navigation pane with the tables and macros hidden.
5. Close and then reopen **U2-BenchmarkPropMgt.accde**.
6. Insert a screenshot of the database in a new Microsoft Word document using the Screenshot button in the Illustrations group on the Insert tab or the Print Screen key and the Paste feature. Type your name a few lines below the screenshot and add any other identifying information as instructed. Print the Word document and then exit Word without saving.

Assessment 6

Export Data from the Property Management Database

1. With **U2-BenchmarkPropMgt.accde** open, export the LeaseTermsAndDeposits query as a text file using the default name and making sure that the file is saved on your storage medium. Include the field names in the first row and remove the quotation marks. Do not save the export steps.
2. Open Notepad, open **LeaseTermsAndDeposits.txt**, and then print the text file.
3. Exit Notepad.
4. Click the button that you created to exit the database.

Writing Activities

The following activities give you the opportunity to practice your writing skills while demonstrating an understanding of some of the important Access features you have mastered in this unit. Use correct grammar, appropriate word choices, and clear sentence constructions.

Activity 1

Create a New Database for Renovation Contracts by Importing Data

You work for a home renovation contractor who operates as a sole proprietor. The contractor has an old computer in his basement that he has been using to keep invoices and other records for renovation contracts. The computer is from the era of the Windows XP operating system and the software on it is no longer being sold or updated. The contractor was able to copy data from the old system into a tab delimited text file named **DavisRenos.txt**.

Create a new Access database named **U2-DavisRenos.accdb** and import the data from the old system into a new table. Modify the table design after importing to apply the Currency format to the *Amount* field. Design and create a form based on the table to be used for entering new records. Also design and create a report to print the records, including a total for the *Invoice Amount* column.

The contractor is not familiar with Access and has asked you to create a user-friendly menu that can be used to add new records via the form you designed and to view the report. Create the menu using a Navigation form and configure startup options so that the menu is the only object that displays in the work area when the database is opened. Test your menu to make sure each tab functions correctly.

Using Microsoft Word, compose a quick reference instruction page for the contractor that instructs him on how to open the database, add a new record, view and print the report, and exit the database. Save the Word document and name it **U2-Act1-DavisRenos**. Print the document.

Activity 2

Design and Publish a Report for a Painting Franchise

A friend who has started a student painting franchise has asked for your help in designing a database to store job information and revenue earned from jobs completed over the summer. Create a new database and save it with the name **U2-StudentPainters**. Design and create tables to store the records for painting contract jobs. For each job, include the date the job was completed; the invoice number; the homeowner name, address, and telephone number; and the contract price. Enter at least 10 records into the tables.

Design a report to print the records in ascending order by date completed. Include statistics at the bottom of the report that provide your friend with the maximum, minimum, average, and total of the contract price field. Include appropriate titles and other report elements. Add your name in the footer as the report designer. Print the report.

Internet Research
Buying a Home

You plan on buying a home within the next few years. While you save money for this investment, you decide to maintain a database of the homes offered for sale within the area you are interested in buying. Design and create tables and relationships in a new database named **U2-Homes4Sale.accdb**. Include fields to store data that will be of interest to you, such as the address, asking price, style of home (condominium, ranch, two story, semidetached, etc.), number of bedrooms, number of bathrooms, type of heating/cooling system, amount of property taxes, and basement and garage information. Design and create a form to be used to enter information into the tables.

Search the Internet to find at least five listings within the area you wish to live and then use the form to enter information for each listing. Design and create a report that groups the records by style of home. Calculate the average asking price at the end of each group and at the end of the report. Include five hyperlinked control objects that will link to the web pages from which you retrieved the information for the listings. Include appropriate titles and other report elements. Add your name in the footer as the report designer. Print the report.

Job Study
Meals on Wheels Database

You are a volunteer working in the office of your local Meals on Wheels organization. Meals on Wheels delivers nutritious, affordable meals to citizens in need of the service, such as seniors, convalescents, and people with disabilities. The organization requires volunteers using their own vehicles to drive to the meal depot, pick up the meals, and deliver them to clients' homes. The volunteer coordinator has expressed an interest in using an Access database to better organize and plan volunteer delivery routes. Create a new database named **U2MealsOnWheels.accdb**. Design and create tables and relationships according to the instructions below. Remember to apply best practices in database design to minimize data redundancy and validate data whenever possible to ensure accuracy.

- TenantsAndLeases form
- Include fields for the client name, address, telephone, gender, age, reason for requiring meals (senior, convalescent, or disability), meals required (breakfast, lunch, dinner), date service started, and estimated length of service required.
- Include fields for the volunteer name, address, telephone, gender, age, date started, availability by day and by meal (breakfast, lunch, dinner), valid driver's license, and receipt of police check clearance.

- Incorporate in your design assignments for the client and the volunteer to the quadrant of the city or town in which each is located. The volunteer coordinator divides the city or town by north, south, east, and west and tries to match drivers with clients in the same quadrant.
- Include other information you think will be important to the volunteer coordinator for this service.

Create a user-defined form template so that all of your forms have a consistent look. Design and create forms to be used to enter the information into the tables and then use the forms to enter at least eight client records and five volunteer records. Make sure you enter records for both clients and volunteers in all four quadrants and for all three meals (breakfast, lunch, dinner). Design and create queries to extract records of clients and volunteers within the same quadrant. Include in the query results datasheet the information you think will be useful to the volunteer coordinator in setting up route schedules. Design and create reports based on the queries. Print the reports.

Create a main menu for the database to provide access to the forms and reports. Configure startup options to display an application title and the main menu form and to hide the tables in the Navigation pane when the database is opened. Close the database and then reopen it. In Word, use the Screenshot button in the Illustrations group on the Insert tab or the Print Screen key with the Paste feature to capture an image of the Access window. Print the image from Word and then exit Word without saving.